Cellular Fine Structure

AN INTRODUCTORY STUDENT TEXT AND ATLAS

JAMES A. FREEMAN, B.S., M.D.

Instructor of Pathology, Louisiana State University
School of Medicine, New Orleans

With the collaboration of

JACK C. GEER, B.S., M.D.

Associate Professor of Pathology,
Louisiana State University
School of Medicine, New Orleans

3386

The Blakiston Division
McGRAW–HILL BOOK COMPANY

NEW YORK   TORONTO   LONDON

DEDICATION

To

Frank N. Low, Ph.D.

An inspiring teacher,
a dedicated researcher,
and, most of all, a fine person.

PREFACE

Our knowledge of biology and its numerous subspecialties has been advanced greatly by electron microscopy which has provided a common meeting place for physics, chemistry, and biology. We have reached a stage where many of the problems of the physicist and the chemist require a knowledge of cytology, and vice versa, for their solution. The electron microscope not only has made possible many new discoveries, but also has modified much of our knowledge and concepts about cells and tissues. Also in the study of disease processes, the current investigative trend is to focus attention on the molecular aspect of disease necessitating a knowledge of the chemistry and fine structure of cell components. It seems logical, therefore, that an attempt should be made to bring together for the student the elementary principles of biological electron microscopy, and to a limited extent biochemical cytology. In planning the text the author has intentionally limited the account to those essentials that a beginner may be expected to master, rather than elucidating minute details that may confuse rather than enlighten. An attempt has been made to present not the views of one man, but the consensus of opinion as presented in the literature. Although the text is concerned primarily with fine structure, some attention has been paid to the chemistry and function of cell components. In this respect the author has maintained the approach of the "new biologist" in attempting to ally structure and function. There is an obvious inconsistency in the amount of information and style of presentation of various chapters, which reflects not only the author's bias, but also the availability of information in the literature on different aspects of cellular fine structure.

This book is organized into three major parts. Part I is devoted to the techniques of electron microscopy and to the interpretation of electron micrographs. Only the basic principles of the techniques are described. Part II is designed to give the student a foundation for recognition of the various components of the cell and Part III describes the tissues of the body. An atlas format is used to provide many of the pictures from which the interpretations were derived.

Numerous line drawings are used in the Part I so the student can obtain a visual idea of the techniques. Many three-dimensional schematic line drawings are used throughout the book. These drawings are not intended to convey the idea that the organization of tissues and cells is exactly as is portrayed in the drawings, but only to give a visual concept as a foundation of understanding structure. The line drawings represent a compilation of the ideas of many investigators. The author must assume the responsibility, however, for faulty interpretation or inexactness in reproduction. Numerous light micrographs and low-magnification electron micrographs are included in an effort to bridge the gap between light and electron microscopy. Successively higher magnifications are provided to permit the ready transition of ideas from light microscopic to macromolecular levels.

This book is not intended to be a complete cytology or to supplant existing text books of histology; it is intended to supplement textbooks of histology by providing for the student a foundation for transition from cellular to molecular realms.

James A. Freeman, M.D.

ACKNOWLEDGMENTS

Scientific books are based on the accumulated data and work of multitudes of scientists and investigators and this book is no exception. To these scientists and investigators, the author expresses his sincere indebtedness.

Mrs. Kathy Phelps and Miss Catherine Catsulis sectioned about seventy-four per cent of the tissues for electron microscopy during the course of this work. The technical excellence of their work in preparation and sectioning of tissues has been of incalculable value. The remainder of the tissues were sectioned, in order of their contribution, by Mr. Ben O. Spurlock, Dr. Juan Takano, Dr. Adele Meyer, and Dr. Benito Galindo. Thanks also are extended to Mrs. Nora White, Mrs. Tommie Sue Tralka, Mrs. Victoria Kattine, and Miss Sharon Russell, who sectioned the tissues for light microscopy. The embedding medium used in the preparation of tissues for electron microscopy was developed by the author and Mr. Ben O. Spurlock.

The advice of Dr. Frank N. Low has been invaluable in planning the book and his painstaking review of the entire manuscript is sincerely appreciated. Also, Dr. Henry C. McGill, Jr. deserves my profound thanks for his constant encouragement, advice, and literary review of the manuscript. Thanks are no less due to Mr. Robert Druce who maintained the electron miscroscopes in the excellent working condition necessary to accomplish the work required to illustrate the text. To Mr. Don Alvarado and Miss Claudia de Gruy I particularly am obliged for the line drawings, which should contribute significantly to the student's grasp of cell fine structure. Mr. Eugene Wolfe spent many hours photographing light microscopic specimens and making the light and electron micrographs.

To him I owe a debt of gratitude.

The animals from which the tissues were taken were provided by many persons who are hereby acknowledged; Drs. Monroe Samuels and John Bickers (blood and bone marrow), Dr. Ronald Welsh (rabbits), Dr. Adele Edison (cats), Mr. Jimmie Leslie (rats), Mr. Doyle Land (guinea pigs). The human tissues were obtained from patients hospitalized at the Charity Hospital of Louisiana.

For typing the many preliminary manuscripts, thanks are extended to Mrs. Dorothy Tripoli, Mrs. Marguerite Robinson, Mrs. Rhea Dupeire, Miss Mary Grace Kelleher, Mrs. Ruth Reynaud, and Mrs. Faith Hornby. Mrs. Jimmy Carney typed the final draft of the manuscript. The kind assistance of the library staff, namely Miss Margaret Rouse, Miss Christa Sykes, Mrs. Mamie Morgan, and Miss Lynne Watson, is hereby acknowledged.

Sincere thanks are given to Dr. Ronald Welsh who permitted me to photograph his sectioned specimens for Chapter 19. Figure 183 was made available by Dr. Benito Galindo from a publication co-authored with the author. Dr. Juan Takano kindly provided Figures 19, 97, and 123, from his own studies during a training course in our laboratory.

During the course of this work the author was a Special Fellow (CSP-16, 118) of the National Institutes of Health, and Dr. Geer was a recipient of a Research Career Development Award (GMK-3-15, 333) from the National Institutes of Health. The laboratories in which this work was done were supported by the National Institutes of Health (grant HE-2549) and Cancer Association of Greater New Orleans (grants 503-62 and 616-63).

James A. Freeman, M.D.

HISTORICAL REVIEW OF ELECTRON MICROSCOPY

1650–O. von Guericke originated the electron (vacuum) tube.

1873–Ernest Abbe showed that the useful resolving power of the light microscope was limited by the wave length of the illumination used, approximately one-half the wave length of light.

1897–F. Braun invented the cathode ray tube.

1897–J. J. Thomson demonstrated the relationship of electrons and cathode ray tube.

1907–C. Stoemer accurately calculated the trajectory of electrons in magnetic fields.

1924–L. V. De Broglie showed that a beam of electrons could be regarded as a wave motion, in similar manner to light optics.

1926–H. Busch demonstrated that a suitably shaped magnetic field could operate as a lens and converge a beam of electrons.

1927–D. Gabor developed an ironclad magnetic lens.

1932–R. Rüdenberg patented the design of an electron microscope in Germany.

1932–E. Brüche and H. Johannson built first electrostatic electron microscope.

1932–M. Knoll and E. Ruska built the first electron microscope model utilizing magnetic lenses.

1934–L. Marton built a simple magnetic electron microscope with which the first biological observations were made.

1935–E. Driest and H. O. Mueller achieved a useful magnification of approximately 5,000 diameters with a resolution greater than that of the light microscope using Knoll's and Ruska's magnetic electron microscope.

1937–L. Marton took the first bacteriological pictures with the electron microscope.

1938–B. von Borries and E. Ruska designed and built an instrument capable of achieving a useful magnification of 20,000 diameters and a resolution of 100 Ångstroms.

1938–A. Prebus and J. Hillier built the first magnetic electron microscope in North America.

1939–Siemens and Halske Company in Germany began commercial production of von Borries' and Ruska's microscope.

1940–The Radio Corporation of America marketed a commercial electron microscope based on Prebus' and Hillier's design.

1940–H. Ruska, using an electron microscope, obtained first pictures of viruses.

1940–H. Mahl produced an electrostatic electron microscope in Germany.

1943–H. Boersch discovered the Fresnel diffraction phenomenon in electron microscope images.

1944–R. Williams and R. W. G. Wyckoff developed technique of shadow casting, thus illustrating profiles of organisms.

1945–V. Zworykin, G. Morton, E. Ramberg, J. Hillier, and A. Vance published their classical text, "Electron Optics and the Electron Microscope."

1946–J. Hiller and E. Ramberg recognized the role of lens astigmatism in limiting high resolution.

1949–S. Newman, E. Borysko and M. Swerdlow introduced methacrylate as an embedding medium for biological electron microscopy.

1950—H. Latta and J. Hartmann introduced glass knives for thin sectioning in electron microscopy.

1952—G. Palade utilized buffered osmium tetroxide as a successful fixative for electron microscopy.

1953—K. Porter and J. Blum introduced a practical microtome for the sectioning of specimens for use in electron microscopy.

1955—C. Hall used "negative staining" to demonstrate the fine structure in viruses.

1956—J. Luft developed permanganate fixation.

1956—O. Maaløe and A. Birch-Andersen achieved success with the epoxy resin, Araldite, in embedding.

1956—E. Kellenberger, W. Schwab and A. Ryter reported a polyester, Vestopal-W, to be a useful embedding medium for electron microscopy.

1960—J. Luft in America and H. Kushida in Japan introduced another epoxy embedding medium, Epon 812.

1960—G. DuPouy, F. Perrier, and L. Durrieu in Toulouse, France, examined living organisms at 650 kv with a new instrument designed for 1.5 mv operation.

1962—J. Freeman and B. Spurlock applied Maraglas epoxy embedding to electron microscopy.

1963—D. Sabatini, K. Bensch, and R. Barnett demonstrated the preservation of cellular fine structure and enzymatic activity with aldehyde fixation of tissues.

Résumé

1920's—Decade of theoretical discussions of electron microscopy.

1930's—Decade of experimental models of the electron microscopes.

1940's—Decade of commercial models of the electron microscopes and ancillary technical instruments.

1950's—Decade of application of the electron microscope to biology.

1960's—"Golden age" of usefulness of the electron microscope.

CONTENTS

Part I

FUNDAMENTAL CONSIDERATIONS

INTRODUCTION

The light microscope was the contribution of the 16th century toward the goal of the visual exploration of matter. The electron microscope represents one of the significant contributions of the 20th century toward this never ending goal. Although the light microscope did not reach its peak of application until two centuries after its development, the electron microscope has reached a comparable level in two decades. This remarkable progress is a reflection of the technical advances in the preparation of tissues for electron microscopy as well as physical advances in the microscope. In order to understand the visual access provided by the electron microscope to the world between the cellular and molecular realms, the student should be acquainted with the technical preparation of tissues for electron microscopy. Moreover, he should appreciate the artifacts inadvertently introduced by the techniques. In any field of endeavor the student must rely on the interpretations of others. However, by having a knowledge of techniques involved in preparation of tissues, and factors concerned in interpretation of studies with the electron microscope, the student can make some of his own observations and interpretations. Part I is intended to supply this basic knowledge.

1

PREPARATION OF TISSUES
FOR ELECTRON MICROSCOPY

The methods of preparation of tissues for examination with the electron microscope are similar to those used for light microscopy. Tissues are fixed in a suitable protoplasmic coagulating solution, dehydrated in organic solvents, embedded in a supporting matrix, and thin sections are cut on a microtome. The tissue sections are mounted on a suitable supporting structure, stained, and then viewed with the microscope. The methods of tissue preparation for electron microscopy, while basically similar to those for light microscopy, differ in specific procedures. The procedural differences are necessitated by: (1) the greater resolving power of the electron microscope (Fig. 1), requiring well prepared tissues; (2) the lower penetrating power of electrons compared with light, requiring thinner sections; and (3) inability to use differential chromatic staining, since we are dealing with electrons and not light. The basic steps in preparation of tissues for electron microscopy are discussed in the following paragraphs.

OBTAINING TISSUE

It is desirable to expose most tissues to the fixing solution as rapidly as possible to avoid postmortem changes. Tissues containing little connective tissue or those in which a fibrous capsule has been stripped may be fixed in situ for electron microscopy. The tissues from which micrographs in this book were made

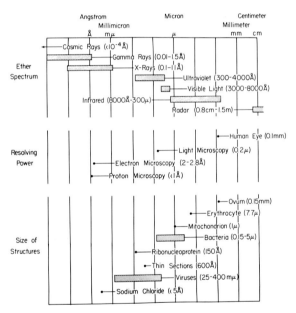

Fig. 1. Comparison of the ether spectrum, resolving power of the human eye and microscopes, and sizes of various structures. The visible portion of the spectrum occupies only a narrow band of wave length about 3000 to 8000 Ångstroms. The light microscope visualizes structures to approximately 0.2 micron. The electron microscope provides magnification and resolving power in the realm of molecular dimensions. Thin sections for electron microscopy are about 600 to 1500 Ångstroms in thickness.

were removed from the animal by sharp dissection and transferred to a drop of fixative on paraffin wax, a non-absorbable surface (Fig. 2). The fixatives most widely used in electron microscopy are slow to penetrate the tissue, and usually penetrate less than 1.0 millimeter into the tissue. Therefore, the pieces of tissues should be diced with a sharp razor blade into fragments no larger than 1.0 millimeter in any dimension (Fig. 3) so that fixation can occur

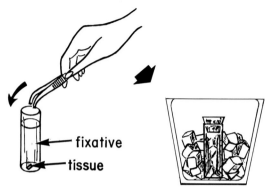

Fig. 4

pended in a fluid, e.g., blood, tissue cultures, the cells are obtained in a pellet by centrifugation and the pellet fixed (Figs. 5 and 6).

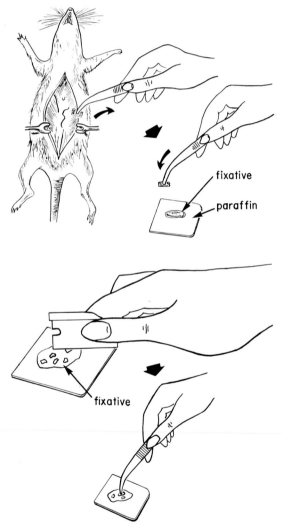

Fig. 3

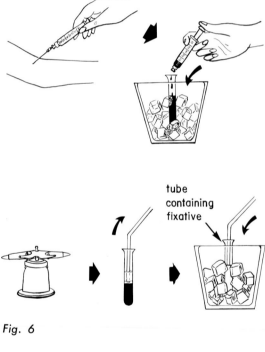

Fig. 6

as quickly as possible. The diced fragments are then transferred to a vial containing cold fresh fixative (Fig. 4). Where cells are sus-

FIXATION

Preservation of tissue by coagulation of as many cellular constituents as possible in as near the living state as possible is the major requirement of an ideal fixative. Osmium tetroxide is the most widely used fixative in electron microscopy and was the fixing agent used for the tissues illustrated in this book. It is the most ideal general fixative known since it fixes more of the cell constituents than any other chemical, and with minimal morphologic change. Diced tissue fragments are fixed in a vial of cold osmium tetroxide (Fig. 4) for ½ to 1 hour, or more, depending on the type of tissue, the purpose of the examination of the tissue, and the preference of the investigator. Fixation at 4 to 10°C is superior to fixation at room temperature. For demonstrating special structures, other fixing agents may be used, such as: buffered potassium permanganate; osmium-chromate mixture; buffered aldehydes, such as formalin, acrolein, and glutaraldehyde; and freeze-substitution. By and large, however, buffered osmium tetroxide is the best general tissue fixative available for electron microscopy.

DEHYDRATION

To embed any tissue in a given medium it is necessary that the medium be miscible with the water present in the tissue, or that the tissue be dehydrated when the embedding medium is not water miscible. Dehydration is achieved by substitution of the water in the tissue with an organic solvent, usually ethanol, that is water miscible. This is accomplished by immersing the tissue in progressively increasing concentrations of ethanol. In electron microscopy, the ethanol is then substituted with a miscible liquid plastic embedding medium in similar progressive steps. Before placing the tissue in the liquid plastic embedding medium, a second dehydrating agent, such as propylene oxide, sometimes is used to insure more complete dehydration.

EMBEDDING

Embedding media provide a supporting matrix for the tissue to facilitate cutting, sectioning, on a microtome. Paraffin and celloidin, the most widely used embedding media in light microscopy, do not provide the hardness or preserve the structural integrity of the tissue

sufficiently for electron microscopy. Therefore, low molecular weight plastics are used as embedding media in electron microscopy. To be a good embedding medium for electron microscopy, a plastic should penetrate the tissue easily and completely, polymerize to the proper hardness without distortion of the tissue structure, be miscible with the dehydrating agent, be sectionable with a microtome without artifact, be relatively stable in the heat of the electron beam (thermostable), and withstand the vacuum of the electron microscope. A variety of plastics are employed, including methacrylates, epoxy resins, and polyesters. The micrographs in this book are taken of sections of tissues embedded in Maraglas *

* Polysciences, Inc., P.O. Box 4, Rydal, Penna.

(an epoxy resin).

After dehydration the tissues are immersed in a dilute solution of plastic with a suitable hardening agent added and then in full-strength plastic. Once the tissues are thoroughly impregnated with the plastic, they are placed in a vessel, usually a gelatin capsule, and fresh plastic is poured into the capsule (Fig. 7). The hardening agents catalyze the

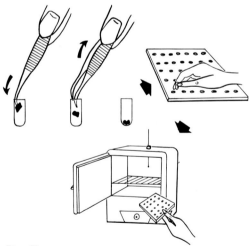

Fig. 7

polymerization of the plastic. Most plastics, including Maraglas, are hardened in an oven with dry heat (Fig. 7) or by ultraviolet irradiation. The final hardness of the plastic-embedded tissue, an important factor in sectioning, can be altered by adding flexibilizing or plasticizing agents to the liquid embedding medium before impregnation of the tissue with the plastic.

A typical schedule for preparation of the tissues illustrated in this book is as follows:

1. Veronal buffered osmium tetroxide (pH-7.4)	30 min.
2. 10 per cent phosphate buffered formalin (ph-7.0)	30 min.
3. 50 per cent ethanol	15 min.
4. 70 per cent ethanol	15 min.
5. 95 per cent ethanol	15 min.
6. Absolute ethanol (2 changes)	15 min. each
7. Propylene oxide (2 changes)	15 min. each
8. Propylene oxide–Maraglas mixture 1:1	30 min.
9. Maraglas mixture (at 10°C)	12 hr.
10. Embedding in gelatin capsules and hardening in 60°C oven	24 to 48 hr.

SECTIONING

The plastic with embedded tissue is trimmed to a small pyramid to provide an exposed rectangular face of tissue about 0.5 millimeter in maximum dimension for sectioning, and is then placed in the microtome chuck (Fig. 8).

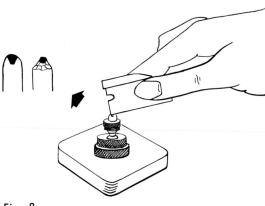

Fig. 8

The principal difference between microtomes used in electron microscopy and microtomes used in light microscopy is the advance mechanism. The advance mechanism of microtomes used for electron microscopy is more finely

calibrated and permits one to cut the extremely thin sections that are necessary because of the lower penetrating ability of the electron beam. Sections for light microscopy are usually 5 to 7 microns in thickness, while those for electron microscopy, often called ultrathin sections, are less than 1000 Ångstroms (0.1 micron) in thickness.

A variety of microtomes are available for cutting thin sections for electron microscopy. Figure 9 is a drawing of a Servall Porter-Blum microtome * which uses a mechanical ad-

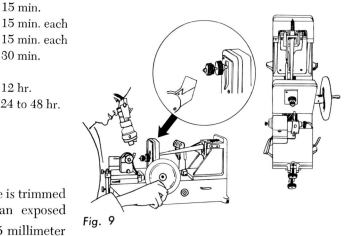

Fig. 9

vance. Other microtomes use a thermal type of advance provided by heating a metal rod on which the chuck with plastic embedded tissue is fitted. In either type of microtome, the knife is advanced to the trimmed tissue face, and then the microtome wheel is turned to cut the thin sections. The sections, as they are cut are lifted from the knife edge and floated on a well containing fluid (Fig. 10). They are

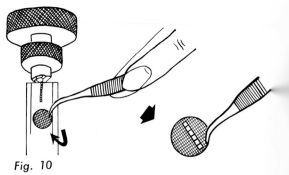

Fig. 10

* Ivan Sorvall, Inc., Norwalk, Conn.

judged for thickness by their interference colors in incident light. Purple or blue sections are too thick; the most desirable (thinnest) sections are silver or a light gold hue.

Special knives are needed to cut thin sections. The knife usually used is fractured plate glass. Glass is an undercooled liquid—a solid material that is not crystalline. This property tends to produce a finer fracture line, hence a sharper cutting edge, than one could achieve with crystalline material, e.g., metal. Glass knives are prepared by scoring thin strips of polished plate glass (⅜ or ¼ inch thick) with a glass cutter, and breaking them into rhomboids with glass-breaking pliers (Fig. 11). As

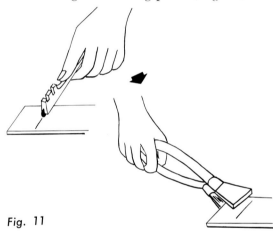

Fig. 11

the very thin sections are cut from the knife edge it is necessary that a fluid medium be present to float the sections upon, so that the sections may be picked up on perforated plastic coated metal discs (analogous to glass slides for light microscopy). A well for fluid is prepared by wrapping masking tape about the peak of the rhomboid and is sealed with melted wax applied with a small brush (Fig. 12). Specially prepared diamonds polished to

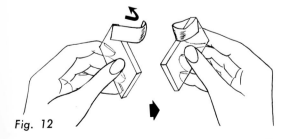

Fig. 12

a very fine edge can also be used to cut thin sections. Although the diamond is a crystalline substance, very sharp edges can be obtained since diamond has perfect cleavage.

MOUNTING

Glass slides are used to support sections for viewing in light microscopy. Since the penetrating power of electrons is small and electrons will not penetrate glass, perforated metal discs (grids) are used to support the sections in electron microscopy (Fig. 10). These discs are available in a wide variety of sizes of perforation. Electrons will readily penetrate the areas of the sections overlying the perforations. If the perforations of the grid are large, the section may fall through the open area, and it is sometimes necessary that the perforation be covered with a thin film of plastic to provide sufficient support for the tissue sections in the electron beam. The plastic films used are usually Formvar or Parlodian. There are a wide variety of methods for coating the grids that can be found in textbooks on electron microscopic techniques.

STAINING

Various components of a tissue can be identified by selective chromatic stains using the light microscope. Chromatic staining is impossible in the electron microscope and structures can only be identified by morphology and electron density. Although chromatic stains are not useful for electron microscopy, there are methods by which many components of a tissue can be identified. Certain structures in a cell may be more clearly visualized (made more or less electron dense compared to their surroundings) by varying fixation procedures or by "electron stains." These stains are solutions of salts of heavy metals, in which the sections on the copper grids are immersed or floated (Fig. 13). The more common electron stains are lead hydroxide, uranyl acetate, uranyl nitrate, and phosphotungstic acid. In the case of certain tissue enzymes, sites of enzymatic activity can be identified in the

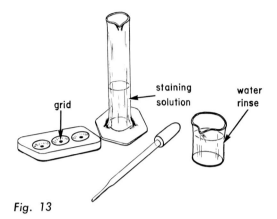

staining
solution

water
rinse

grid

Fig. 13

electron microscope by allowing a block of tissue or a section to react with the proper substrate, and then reacting the product of the enzymatic reaction with an appropriate heavy metal compound. The metal compound is precipitated, and this part of the tissue is increased in density. Certain chemicals may be identified in the electron microscope if the chemical, radioactively labeled, is incorporated into the cell. A tissue section of the radioactively labeled cell is covered with a thin film of fine grain photographic emulsion. The radioactivity reduces the silver in the photographic emulsion, and thus provides a locus of high electron density.

VIEWING

To view the section one has prepared, the grid on which it is mounted is inserted into the column of the electron microscope between the condenser and objective lenses—in position similar to that in the light microscope. Since electrons will be scattered by atoms with which they collide, it is necessary to operate the column of the electron microscope in a vacuum (approximately 1×10^{-4} millimeters Hg) to prevent scattering of the electron beam by the atoms in the air. Most living matter will not survive in such a vacuum, and therefore tissue usually is fixed before it can be examined in the electron microscope.

The basic difference in the formation of the image viewed in the two types of microscopes is that the photons and optical lenses of the light microscope are electrons and magnetic lenses of the electron microscope. The final image seen by the observer in the electron microscope is formed by electrons impinging on a phosphorescent screen that is thus stimulated to emit photons visible to the human eye. This is a basic phenomenon with which everyone is familiar—in the television picture tube, the image is formed in the same manner. The micrographs used in this book were made from specimens examined and photographed in RCA* EMU-3c and EMU-3f electron microscopes.

* Radio Corporation of America, Camden, N.J.

REFERENCES

General

Kay, D.: *Techniques for Electron Microscopy.* Blackwell Scientific Publications, Oxford, 1961.

Mercer, E., and M. Birbeck: *Electron Microscopy: A Handbook for Biologists.* Blackwell Scientific Publications, Oxford, 1961.

Pease, D.: *Histological Techniques for Electron Microscopy.* Academic Press, Inc., New York, 1960.

Selby, C.: Electron microscopy: Techniques and applications in cytology, in *Analytical Cytology,* 2nd edition, edited by R. Mellors, pp. 273–341. McGraw-Hill Book Company, New York, 1959.

Wischnitzer, S.: *Introduction to Electron Microscopy.* Pergamon Press, New York, 1962.

Obtaining Tissue

Low, F., and J. Freeman: *Electron Microscopic Atlas of Normal and Leukemic Human Blood,* pp. 1–2. McGraw-Hill Book Company, New York, 1958.

Palade, G.: A study of fixation for electron microscopy. J. Exper. Med., **95**:285–298, 1952.

Fixation and Dehydration

Bahr, G.: Continued studies about the fixation with osmium tetroxide. Exper. Cell Res., **9**:277–285, 1955.

Caulfield, J. B.: Effects of varying the vehicle for OsO_4 in tissue fixation. J. Biophys. Biochem. Cytol., **3**:827–830, 1957.

Dalton, A.: A chrome-osmium fixative for electron microscopy. Anat. Rec., **121**:281, 1955.

FERNÁNDEZ-MORÁN, H.: Low-temperature preparation technique for electron microscopy of biological specimens based on rapid freezing with liquid helium II. Ann. New York Acad. Sci., **85**:689–713, 1960.

HOLT, S., and R. HICKS: Studies on formalin fixation for electron microscopy and cytochemical staining purposes. J. Biophys. Biochem. Cytol., **11**:37–45, 1961.

LUFT, J. H.: Permanganate—a new fixative for electron microscopy. J. Biophys. Biochem. Cytol., **2**: 799–802, 1956.

MILLONIG, G.: Advantages of a phosphate buffer for OsO₄ solutions in fixation. J. Appl. Phys., **32**:1637, 1961.

PALADE, G.: A study of fixation for electron microscopy. J. Exper. Med., **95**:285–298, 1952.

PORTER, K., and F. KALLMAN: The properties and effects of osmium tetroxide as a tissue fixative with special reference to its use for electron microscopy. Exper. Cell Res., **4**:127–141, 1953.

SABATINI, D., K. BENSCH, and R. BARNETT: Cytochemistry and electron microscopy. The preservation of cellular ultrastructure and enzymatic activity by aldehyde fixation. J. Cell Biol., **17**:19–58, 1963.

Embedding

FINCK, HENRY: Epoxy resins in electron microscopy. J. Biophys. Biochem. Cytol., **7**:27–30, 1960.

FREEMAN, J., and B. SPURLOCK: A new epoxy embedment for electron microscopy. J. Cell Biol., **13**:437–443, 1962.

FREEMAN, J.: Maraglas epoxy embedding. Sci. Insts. News, **8**:9–12, 1963.

GIBBONS, I.: An embedding resin miscible with water for electron microscopy. Nature, **184**:375–376, 1959.

KUSHIDA, H.: On the handling of epoxy resins and polyester resins as embedding media for electron microscopy. J. Electronmic., **9**:157–158, 1960.

LOW, F. N., and M. CLEVENGER: Polyester-methacrylate embedments for electron microscopy. J. Cell Biol., **12**:615–621, 1962.

LUFT, J. H.: Improvements in epoxy resin embedding methods. J. Biophys. Biochem. Cytol., **9**:409–414, 1961.

NEWMAN, S., and E. BORYSKO, and M. SWERDLOW: New sectioning techniques for light and electron microscopy. Science, **110**(2846):66–68, 1949.

RYTER, A., and E. KELLENBERGER: L'inclusion au polyester pour l'ultramicrotomie. J. Ultrast. Res., **2**:200–214, 1958.

STRÄUBLI, W.: Nouvelle matière d'inclusion hydrosoluble pour la cytologie électronique. Compt. Rend. Acad. Sci., **250**:1137, 1960.

Sectioning and Mounting

FERNÁNDEZ-MORÁN, H.: A diamond knife for ultrathin sectioning. Exper. Cell Res., **5**:255–256, 1953.

LATTA, H., and J. HARTMANN: Use of a glass edge in thin sectioning for electron microscopy. Proc. Soc. Exper. Biol. & Med., **74**:436–439, 1950.

MORGAN, C., D. MOORE, and H. ROSE: Some effects of the microtome knife and electron beam on methacrylate-embedded thin sections. J. Biophys. Biochem. Cytol., Suppl., **2**:21–28, 1956.

PEACHY, L.: Thin sections. I. A study of section thickness and physical distortion produced during microtomy. J. Biophys. Biochem. Cytol., **4**:233–242, 1958.

PORTER, K., and J. BLUM: A study in microtomy for electron microscopy. Anat. Rec., **117**:685–712, 1953.

WATSON, M.: Carbon films and specimen stability. J. Biophys. Biochem. Cytol., Suppl., **2**:31–36, 1956.

WILLIAMS, R., and F. KALLMAN: Interpretations of electron micrographs of single and serial sections. J. Biophys. Biochem. Cytol., **1**:301–314, 1955.

Staining

BRENNER, S., and R. HORNE: A negative staining method for high resolution electron microscopy of viruses. Biochem. Biophys. Acta, **35**:103–110, 1959.

CARO, L.: Electron microscopic radioautography of thin sections: The Golgi zone as a site of protein concentration in pancreatic acinar cells. J. Biophys. Biochem. Cytol., **10**:37–45, 1961.

HOLT, S., and R. HICKS: Specific staining methods for enzyme localization at the subcellular level. Brit. Med. Bull., **18**:214–219, 1962.

LEDUC, E., and W. BERNHARD: Ultrastructural cytochemistry. Enzyme and acid hydrolysis of nucleic acids and protein. J. Biophys. Biochem. Cytol., **10**:437–455, 1961.

MILLONIG, G.: A modified procedure for lead staining of thin sections. J. Biophys. Biochem. Cytol., **11**:736–739, 1961.

SHELDON, H., H. ZETTERQUIST, and D. BRANDES: Histochemical reactions for electron microscopy: Acid phosphatase. Exper. Cell Res., **9**:592–596, 1955.

SRIRAM, J., S. TAWDE, G. PIERCE, JR., and A. MIDGELEY, JR.: Preparation of antibody-ferritin conjugates for immuno-electron microscopy. J. Cell Biol., **17**:673–674, 1963.

WATSON, M. Staining of tissue sections for electron microscopy with heavy metals. J. Biophys. Biochem. Cytol., **4**:257–270, 1958.

Viewing

AGAR, A.: The operation of the electron microscope, in *Techniques for Electron Microscopy*, edited by D. Kay, pp. 1–31. Blackwell Scientific Publications, Oxford, 1961.

HILLIER, J.: Some considerations of photographic exposure time in the electron microscope. Sci. Insts. News, 1:5–6, 1956.

MARTIN, H., and H. ALLRED: Darkroom techniques in photomicroscopy. Sci. Insts. News, 3:15–20, 1958.

2

DIFFERENCES BETWEEN ELECTRON AND LIGHT MICROGRAPHS

The wealth of detail seen in electron micrographs is primarily a function of the high resolution possible in the electron microscope, which, in turn, is a function of the thinness of the sectioned specimen and the wave length of the electrons of the microscope. Consequently the most important differences between the electron and light photomicrographs (micrographs) are traceable to the difference in thickness of the sectioned specimens, and the difference in the optical systems of the electron and light microscopes.

Given a cell that is 10 microns in diameter it would be theoretically possible to obtain more than 200 thin sections for observation in the electron microscope. As seen in Figure 14, where only four sections have been cut in various planes from a single cell, one might conclude that the cell has no nucleus (C); that it has two nuclei (D); that the nucleus is large and ovoid (B); or that the nucleus is small and ovoid (A). In only one plane is the nucleolus sectioned (D). To obtain a true concept of cellular shape and all the organelles in the cell, it would be necessary to section serially and reconstruct the cell, a difficult technical procedure. In electron microscopy, it is usually necessary to make multiple observations with multiple sections to obtain a concept of structure. Certain organelles, such as mitochondria, however, may be small enough to section serially, so that a true picture of the size, shape, and structure of the organelle may be obtained. Moreover, the presence of a round structure in a particular section does not mean necessarily that it is a sphere in three dimensions. It may be a cylinder or a variety of other shapes that could appear round in only one plane. It must be remembered, furthermore, that failure to visu-

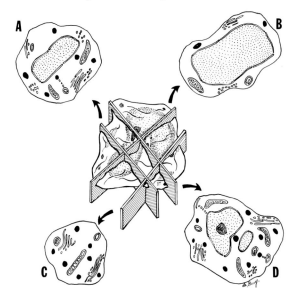

Fig. 14. Single cell (center) randomly sectioned in four planes, thus creating distinctly different pictures. (Redrawn and modified from F. Low and J. Freeman, "Electron Microscopic Atlas of Normal and Leukemic Human Blood," McGraw-Hill Book Company, New York, 1958.)

11

alize a certain structure in an electron micrograph is not proof that the cell has no such structure, as it may lie in another plane of section.

Since most light microscopic sections are 5 to 7 microns in thickness and the depth of field (thickness of clear focus or axial resolution) of the light microscope at high magnification is about 0.2 micron, it is possible to study different levels in a section by changing focus. Only those structures within the depth of field will be in clear focus at any one time. Since the lateral resolution is also 0.2 micron there is no superimposition of particles in the image. At the top of Figure 15, a 5 micron

thick section viewed from one end, i.e., a section in cross-section, is demonstrated. The depth of field of a light microscope is drawn through the center of the section, and the image that would be formed from this is drawn below. Two of the structures are not seen at all in the viewed image, and the others are clearly separate from one another. Figure 16 depicts a $\frac{1}{15}$ micron (670 Ångstroms) section as it would be seen with an electron beam forming the image. Since the depth of field of the electron microscope (usually about 1 micron) is greater than the thickness of this section, all the structures will appear in the viewed image, and some would be super-

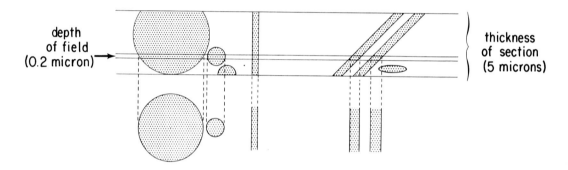

Fig. 15. Depth of field is only a fraction of specimen thickness in light microscopy. Therefore only a small portion of specimen is viewed at any one time. Compare with Fig. 16. (Redrawn and modified from F. Low, *Anat. Rec.,* **117**:244, 1953.)

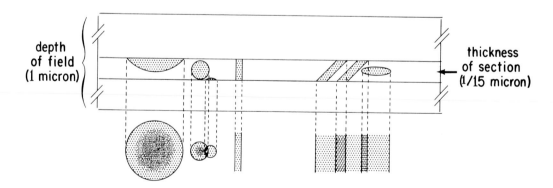

Fig. 16. Depth of field of electron microscope is much greater than thickness of sectioned specimen. Therefore entire section will be visible in one plane, and superimposition of images of various structures can occur. Compare with Figure 15. (Redrawn and modified from F. Low, *Anat. Rec.* **117**:244, 1953.)

imposed. The three circular structures overlap and could be erroneously interpreted as a single structure or structures within structures. Only the vertical membranes form a reliable image. The diagonal membranes and ovoid membranes on the right appear to be one within another while in fact they are separate and distinct. This feature of sectioned specimens must be borne in mind when making interpretations of electron micrographs.

The method by which the electron microscope forms an image is quite similar to that for the light microscope (Fig. 17). In place of an incandescent lamp the electron micro-

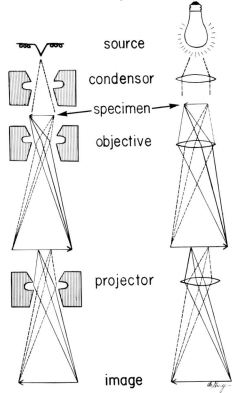

source

condensor

specimen

objective

projector

image

Fig. 17. Comparison of the basic structure of electron and light microscopes.

scope has a tungsten filament that is heated to provide a source of electrons. Light travels at high speed in all directions from its source; electrons do not. Electrons must be accelerated through the microcope by a high voltage in the region of the source. The beam of accelerated electrons first passes the con-

denser lens that spreads or condenses the beam. In effect, the condenser varies the amount of illumination one can obtain. The electron beam then passes through the tissue section suspended in the objective lens. With the light microscope focus is obtained by raising or lowering the objective lens. By varying the current in the objective lens of the electron microscope the image of the specimen is focused. The image from the objective lens of the electron microscope then passes through the projector lens. By varying the current in the projector lens the size of the projected image can be varied—magnification is changed. The projector lens of the electron microscope is analogous to the ocular lens of a light microscope. Ordinarily in light microscopy, however, we change the objective lens to change magnification rather than changing ocular lenses. Whereas the light microscope uses glass lenses through which light passes (Fig. 17) and changing the distance of the lenses from the specimen enables one to form the desired image, the lenses of the electron microscope are hollow magnets through which electrons pass (Fig. 17) and the desired image is produced by changing the electrical current flowing through the lenses, thus changing the magnetic field.

REFERENCES

Agar, A.: Interpretation of electron micrographs, in *Techniques for Electron Microscopy*, edited by D. Kay, pp. 26–29. Blackwell Scientific Publications, Oxford, 1961.

Low, F. N.: The pulmonary alveolar epithelium of laboratory mammals and man. Anat. Rec., **117**:241–264, 1953.

Low, F., and J. Freeman: *Electron Microscopic Atlas of Normal and Leukemic Human Blood*, pp. 2–7. McGraw-Hill Book Company, New York, 1958.

Reissner, J.: Instrumental factors involved in the improvement of contrast in electron microscopy. Sci. Insts. News, **5**:26–32, 1960.

Williams, R., and F. Kallman: Interpretations of electron micrographs of single and serial sections. J. Biophys. Biochem. Cytol., **1**:301–314, 1955.

Wischnitzer, S.: *Introduction to Electron Microscopy*, pp. 1–2 and 29–30. Pergamon Press, New York, 1962.

THE CELL

INTRODUCTION

In the traditional concept of the typical cell a generation ago, the cellular organelles such as the mitochondria were depicted as solid structures embedded in a cytoplasmic matrix. The only membranes shown were the cell membrane and the nuclear membrane. Electron microscopic studies have demonstrated a membranous structure of cell organelles, as well as the cell membrane and the nuclear membrane. Furthermore, the electron microscope has enabled visualization of numerous membranous components of cells that were not suspected to exist where cell structure was studied only with the light microscope. Today, membranes dominate a modern representation of the cell. Part II considers the basic components of the cell with particular emphasis on their membranous nature.

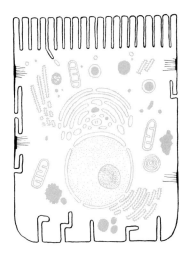

3

PLASMA MEMBRANE
AND
ITS MODIFICATIONS

The cell membrane (*plasmalemma, plasma membrane*) is the structural barrier between the cytoplasm and the external environment of the cell. Its chemical and physical characteristics control the passage of materials into and out of the cell, i.e., *plasma membrane permeability*.

In low magnification electron micrographs the plasma membrane appears as a single dense line limiting the cytoplasm (Fig. 18). At higher magnification, however, the membrane is seen to be a trilaminar structure, two dense lines with a central clear zone. The appearance of the central clear zone with two limiting dense lines is thought to represent the chemical organization of the membrane, namely, a bimolecular leaflet of lipid covered with protein. In specimens fixed with osmium tetroxide the dense outer lines, *outer laminae*, are each about 30 Ångstroms thick, and the clear central zone is about 60 Ångstroms wide. Variability in the thickness of the membrane or of each of its components may normally occur from one cell type to another or as a result of the environment of the cell. Measurements on cells fixed with potassium permanganate show the limiting dense lines to be each about 20 Ångstroms thick; and the central clear zone, about 35 Ångstroms wide. This discrepancy is probably due to differences in the way in which osmium and per-

manganate fix tissue lipoproteins. By x-ray diffraction the total thickness of the plasma membrane in vivo has been estimated to be 200 Ångstroms.

The characteristic combination of two dense lines limiting a central clear zone has been suggested by Robertson to be the fundamental structure of all the membranous parts of cell components (plasma membrane, mitochondria, endoplasmic reticulum, etc.) and has been termed the *unit membrane*. While all membranes have a similar morphology they probably do not possess identical chemical composition, since those limiting the cytoplasm serve a different function than those in mitochondria or endoplasmic reticulum.

There are many structures in which the plasma membrane is modified from a simple smooth limiting membrane into complex forms for special functions. The following are some of these specializations of the plasma membrane.

MICROVILLI

The striated border of the intestinal epithelium was a subject of study for microscopists for over a century, but the structure of this modified cell surface was not appreciated until the electron microscope made visualization at high magnification possible. As can be seen

17

Fig. 18. Cuboidal cell with microvilli on surface of plasma membrane. Junctional complexes are present between adjacent cells (brackets). Dog thyroid. $\times$ 33,000.

Fig. 19. Regular finger-like projections (*microvilli*) constitute the striated border of certain absorptive epithelial cells. Rat ileum. $\times$ 26,000.

Fig. 20. Desmosomes between squamous epithelial cells. Fine fibrils (*cell web*) converge onto the dense thickening of each plasma membrane. Dog esophagus. $\times$ 28,000.

Fig. 18.

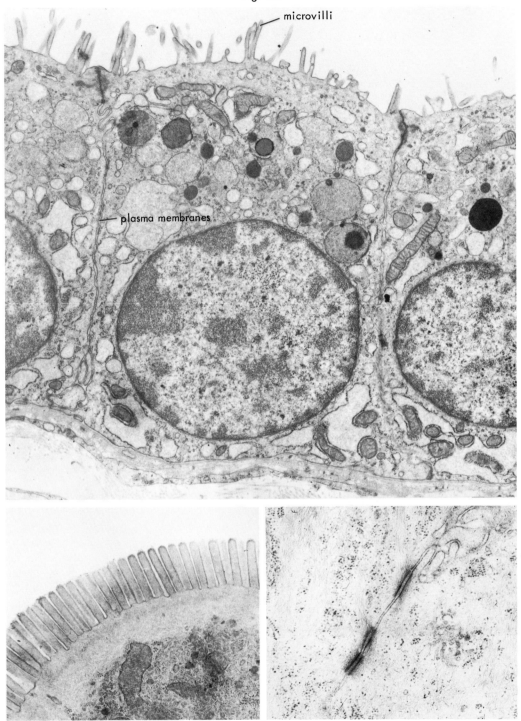

Fig. 19.   Fig. 20.

in Figure 19, the luminal surface of the cell is thrown into numerous folds forming minute villi called *microvilli.* Occasional cells have vertical dense streaks (*rootlets*) which extend from the cytoplasm into the microvilli. The microvilli are about 80 to 100 millimicrons in diameter and 0.6 to 0.8 microns in length. Figure 21 is a three-dimensional schematic representation of microvilli. There is general agreement that this modification of the plasma membrane functions to increase the surface area of the cell, augmenting transport of materials across the plasma membrane. It has been estimated that a single cell may have 3,000 microvilli, and that a square millimeter of intestinal mucosa may have as many as 200 million. Microvilli are found in many cell types: intestinal, renal, uterine, and yolk sac epithelia; mesothelium; and bile canaliculi, to mention but a few. However, the microvilli of the intestinal epithelium have the most constant and typical structure (Fig. 97).

All the microvilli of the intestinal epithelium have the same length, are independent of each other, and do not branch (*striated border*) (Fig. 19). The microvilli of renal tubular epithelium, however, vary greatly in length and some may branch (*brush border*) as seen in Fig. 22. It has been estimated that there are about 128 microvilli per square micron of brush border and that the total surface of the brush border of the two kidneys could amount to 50 or 60 square meters. This enormous absorptive surface area might account, in part, for the extraordinary capacity for the kidney tubules to concentrate the glomerular filtrate and form urine.

CILIA AND FLAGELLA

Contractile filaments are a motile form of surface specialization of cells. They are called *flagella* if they are few in number and long, and *cilia* if they are numerous and short. This modification represents the greatest structural differentiation of the free surface of any epithelium. Between the extremes of number and length there are many intermediate examples, but in all cases the morphology is similar. Like many of the other structures in a cell, cilia and flagella had been studied by light microscopists for many years and there were points of disagreement regarding their fundamental structure. One interesting observation of light microscopists was the birefringence of cilia and flagella which was interpreted to be a result of submicroscopic fibrils oriented in the longitudinal axis. Using the electron microscope Fawcett has revealed nine peripherally placed longitudinal filaments and two central longitudinal filaments, thus confirming the hypothesis of the light microscopists (Figs. 23 to 29). Motile cilia throughout the animal kingdom seem to have this basic "9 + 2" filament structure, but the intracellular portion of the ciliary apparatus differs from one species to another. At the base of each cilium is a basal body, *basal corpuscle,* that bears a striking resemblance to a centriole (Figs. 24 and 28). In some species the longitudinal filaments terminate in the basal body, while in other species the filaments end on a plate distinct from the basal body. Fine fibrillar rootlets, some of which have an axial cross banding at 660 to 700 Ångstrom intervals, extend from the basal body into the cytoplasm (Figs. 24 and 28). The precise mechanism of ciliary movement is not known.

Irregular branching surface modifications of the ductus epididymis have been called *stereocilia.* The stereocilia are actually microvilli

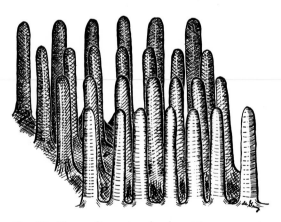

Fig. 21. Three dimensional schematic representation of microvilli.

and not cilia since they do not have the characteristic $9 + 2$ filament structure and they are non-motile.

In the retina the connection between the outer and inner segment of the rods and cones is morphologically identical to a cilium (Fig. 28). It has been postulated that in the histogenesis of the retina the complex structure of the outer segment of rods and cones develops from cilia (Figs. 29 and 30). The crown cells of the saccus vasculosus of the third ventricle of fishes, and the sensory cells of the pineal eye of lizards also have a ciliary structure.

JUNCTIONAL COMPLEXES

Light microscopists have long appreciated that in certain tissues the cells possess points of firm attachment to one another. This is easily demonstrated in the stratum spinosum of the squamous epithelium of the skin where these attachments have been called *intercellular bridges.* In these areas it was thought that "tonofibrils" passed from the cytoplasm of one cell to the other thus forming the areas of firm attachment. With the electron microscope it has been shown that there is no continuity between cells and the tonofibrils actually do not pass from one cell to the other. The zone of attachment, however, is a reality. As seen with the electron microscope this zone has a very characteristic appearance and is referred to as a *desmosome* (granules of Ranvier, nodes of Bizzozero). Desmosomes are discs that appear as electron dense, discontinuous thickenings of apposing plasma membranes (Figs. 20 and 33). The discs are ellipsoidal in shape, measuring 250 to 410 millimicrons in their greatest dimension. Tufts of fine filaments converge onto the desmosomes from the cell cytoplasm (Figs. 20 and 33). The tonofibrils and the cell web recognized by light microscopists are probably aggregates of these filaments. Between the two dense membranes comprising the desmosome is an intercellular space approximately 200 to 240 Ångstroms wide, presumed to be filled with "ground substance."

Desmosomes are not the sites of the terminal bars seen in light microscopy. Desmosomes are found in the juxtaluminal portion of the cell, whereas the terminal bars are closer to the lumen, and probably correspond to areas of close apposition (*zonula adhaerens*) and fusion (*zonula occludens*) of the plasma membrane (Fig. 18). The latter two areas form a continuous belt-like junction immediately beyond the luminal or apical portion of the plasma membrane. The zonula occludens is an area of fusion of adjacent plasma membranes, obliterating the intercellular space, and forming a tight junction. The desmosome is only a point of mechanical attachment of cells, whereas the zonula occludens seals the intercellular space from the contents of the cavity or lumen lined by the epithelium. Therefore the surfaces of contiguous cells are attached and sealed in only restricted areas known as junctional complexes which include the desmosome or macula adhaerens, zonula adhaerens, and zonula occludens, and cells are not cemented together over extensive portions of the plasma membrane as has been implied by light microscopic studies (Fig. 18).

INTERDIGITATIONS OF CONFRONTED CELL SURFACES

Where one cell is closely apposed to another cell, the plasma membranes of the cells may demonstrate complex infolding and interdigitation (Figs. 31 and 32). Such folding increases the surface area of the plasma membrane of the cell. The interdigitation may facilitate the transport of materials into or out of a cell (such as in salivary duct epithelium and renal tubular epithelium), or provide a reserve of cell surface area to accommodate expansion of a cavity (such as in urinary bladder epithelium and partially keratinized squamous epithelium). The spaces found between the complex interdigitations of the cells lining the cervix and vagina apparently are true intercellular channels which exist in life and in all probability are functionally important pathways in the nutrition and metabolism of the epithelium.

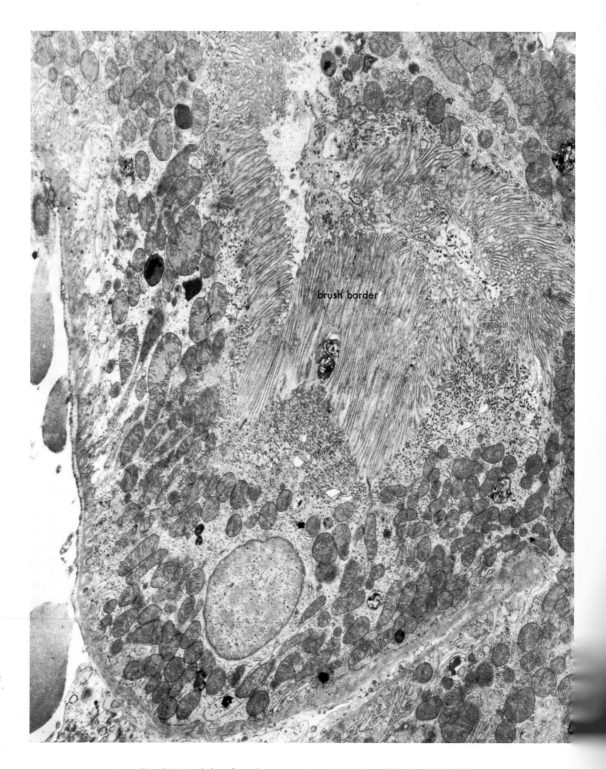

Fig. 22. Brush border of proximal renal tubule cells. Rat. $\times$ 7,400.

Fig. 23.

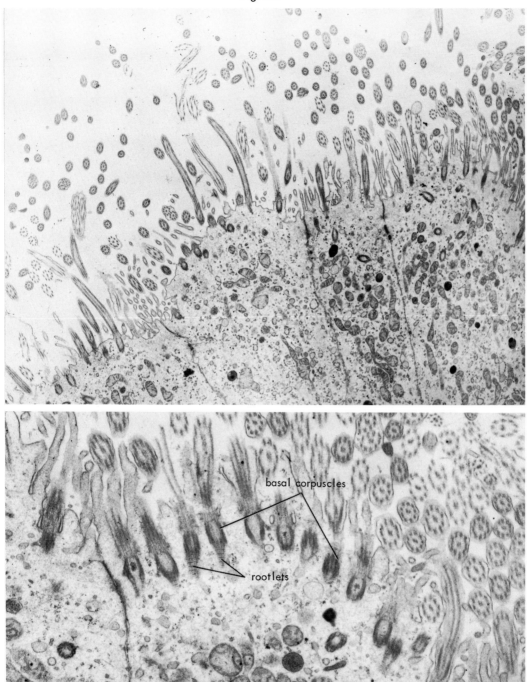

Fig. 24.

Fig. 23. Cilia on the surface of dog tracheal epithelium. $\times$ 9,000.

Fig. 24. Higher magnification of the surface of dog tracheal epithelium showing basal corpuscles of cilia and rootlets with axial periodicity. $\times$ 14,000.

Fig. 25. Tail (*flagellum*) of rat sperm. $\times$ 6,300.

Fig. 26. Longitudinal section of rat sperm tail showing internal filaments of flagella. Also note spiral mitochondria. $\times$ 21,000.

Fig. 27. Cross section of rat sperm tail showing basic "9 + 2" filament structure characteristic of cilia, flagella, and centrioles. $\times$ 21,000.

Fig. 25.

Fig. 26.

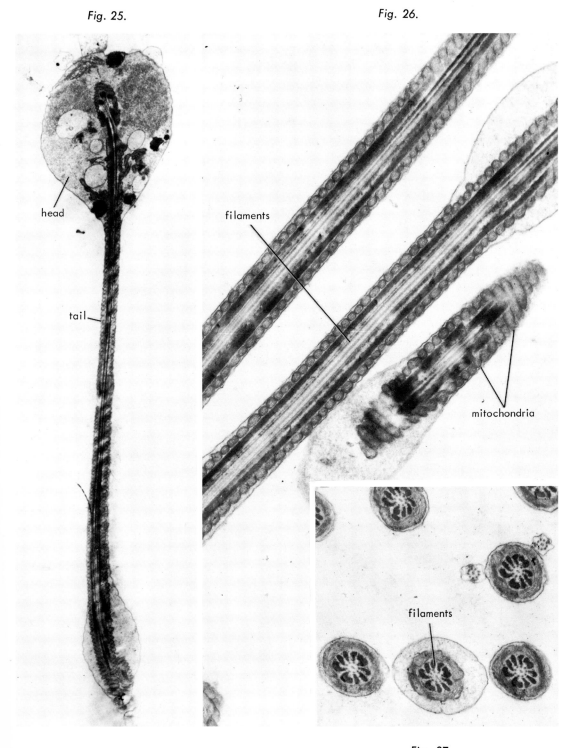

head

tail

filaments

mitochondria

filaments

Fig. 27.

Fig. 28. Connecting cilia between inner and outer segments of rods and cones. Note axial periodicity of basal body of cilia. Dog retina. $\times$ 16,000.

Fig. 29. The outer segments of retinal rods and cones with a connecting cilium. $\times$ 45,000.

Fig. 30. Three-dimensional schematic representation of retinal rod showing relationship of internal filaments to outer and inner segments of rod.

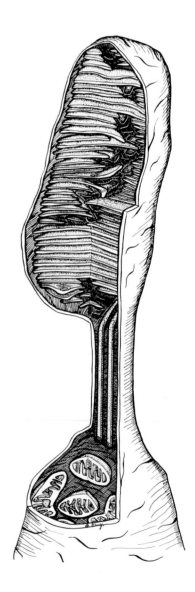

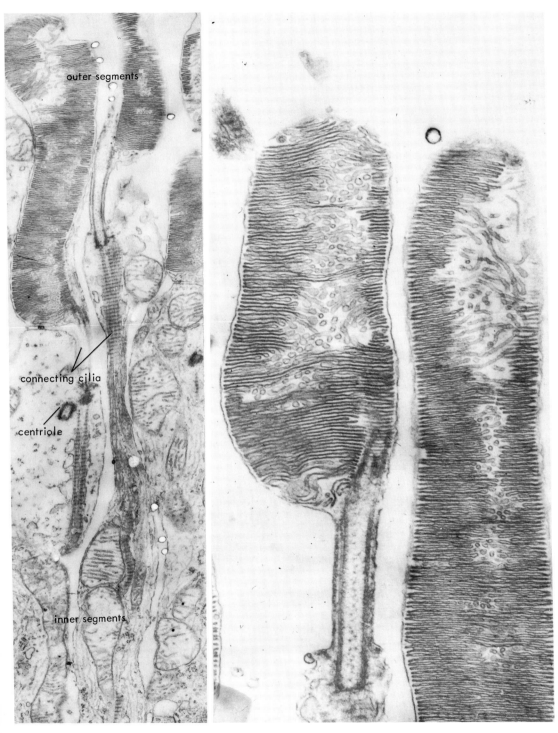

Fig. 28.

Fig. 29.

Fig. 31.

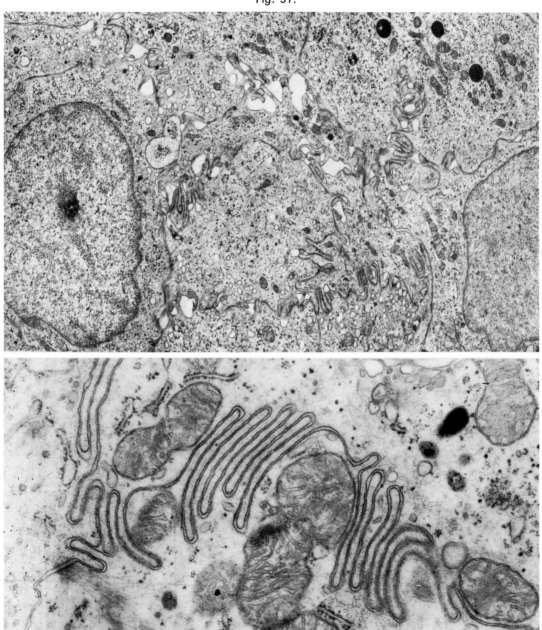

Fig. 32.

Fig. 31. Complex interdigitations of lateral cell membranes in transitional epithelial cells. Dog ureter. × 6,800.

Fig. 32. High magnification of interdigitations of apposing plasma membranes. Guinea pig salivary gland duct epithelium. × 40,000.

Fig. 33.

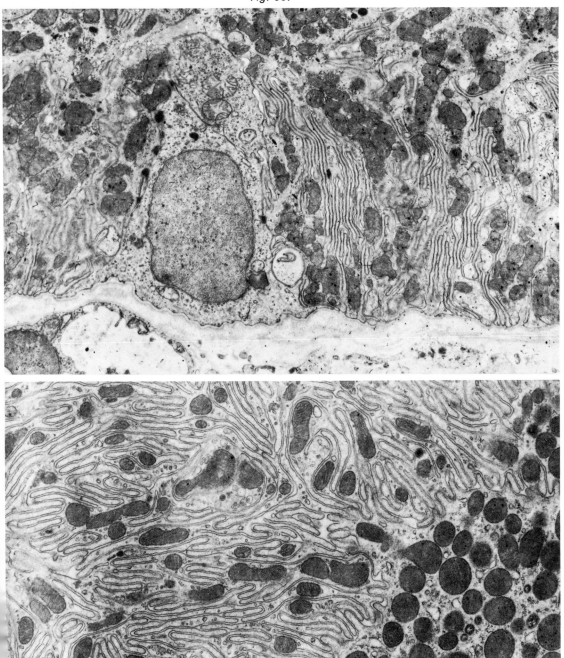

Fig. 34.

Fig. 33. Complex infoldings of basal plasma membrane of epithelial cells noted for water transport. Guinea pig salivary gland duct epithelium. × 8,600.

Fig. 34. Tangential section of basal infolding of plasma membrane of proximal tubule. Rat kidney. × 7,200.

BASILAR MODIFICATIONS

The basilar portion of the plasma membrane of epithelial cells exhibits varying complexity of folding and interdigitation with adjacent cells. The cells may have foot-like processes of cytoplasm that extend from the body of the cell and interdigitate with adjacent cells, such as in salivary duct epithelium (Fig. 33). In renal tubular epithelium, the base of the cell demonstrates numerous invaginations of the plasma membrane that extend into the body of the cell (Fig. 34). Such a pattern is characteristic of cells known for their water transport. The modifications of the basilar portion of the cell increase the surface area, and this increased area is presumed to enhance transport of materials into and out of the cell, especially water. Reciprocal interdigitations between the bases of epithelial cells can advance and retract during life, depending on the amount of fluid, largely water, that collects during metabolism, and thereby can create reservoirs for fluid metabolic products.

REFERENCES

Dalton, A., H. Kahler, and B. Lloyd: The structure of the free surface of a series of epithelial cell types in the mouse as revealed by the electron microscope. Anat. Rec., 111:67–72, 1951.

Farquhar, M., and G. Palade: Junctional complexes in various epithelia. J. Cell Biol., 17:375–412, 1963.

Fawcett, D. W., and K. Porter: A study of the fine structures of ciliated epithelia. J. Morph., 94:221–282, 1954.

Fawcett, D.: Structural specializations of the cell surface, in *Frontiers in Cytology*, edited by S. Palay, pp. 19–41. Yale University Press, New Haven, 1958.

Fawcett, D.: Intercellular bridges. Exper. Cell Res., Suppl., 8:174–187, 1961.

Fawcett, D.: Cilia and flagella, in *The Cell*, vol. II, edited by J. Brachet and A. Mirsky, pp. 217–297. Academic Press, Inc., New York, 1961.

Fawcett, D.: The membranes of the cytoplasm. Lab. Invest., 10:1162–1188, 1961.

Fernández-Morán, H.: Fine structure of biological lamellar systems, in *Biophysical Science—A Study Program*, edited by J. Oncley, F. Schmitt, R. Williams, M. Rosenberg, and R. Bolt, pp. 319–330. John Wiley & Sons, New York, 1959.

Finean, J.: *Chemical Ultrastructure in Living Tissues*, pp. 60–105, Charles C Thomas, Springfield, 1961.

Hama, K.: The fine structure of the desmosomes in frog mesothelium. J. Biophys. Biochem. Cytol., 7:575–576, 1960.

Hogben, A.: Ultrastructure and transport across epithelial membranes. Circulation, 26:1179–1188, 1962.

Pease, D.: Infolded basal plasma membranes found in epithelia noted for their water transport. J. Biophys. Biochem. Cytol., Suppl., 2:203–208, 1956.

Ponder, E.: The cell membrane and its properties, in *The Cell*, vol. II, edited by J. Brachet and A. Mirsky, pp. 1–84. Academic Press, Inc., New York, 1961.

Robertson, J. D.: The membrane of the living cell. Sci. Amer., 206:64–72, April 1962.

Satir, P.: On the evolutionary stability of the 9 + 2 pattern. J. Cell Biol., 12:181–184, 1962.

Stoeckenius, W.: Structure of the plasma membrane. An electron-microscope study. Circulation, 26:1066–1069, 1962.

Tamarin, A., and L. Sreebny: An analysis of desmosome shape, size, and orientation by the use of histometric and densitometric methods with electron microscopy. J. Cell Biol., 18:125–134, 1963.

Weiss, P.: Cell contact. Intern. Rev. Cytol., 7:391–423, 1958.

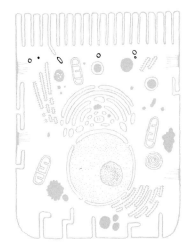

4 PINOCYTOSIS

A process whereby substances are moved from the extracellular medium into the cell was designated *pinocytosis* (from the Greek meaning "cell drinking") by Lewis in 1931. Lewis, observing living cells in tissue culture, noted that the plasma membrane of cytoplasmic pseudopods would enclose and fuse around fluid "globules," with subsequent incorporation of the fluid into the cell cytoplasm. This process is closely akin to the phenomenon of phagocytosis in which a foreign material is incorporated into the cell. In pinocytosis, however, a droplet of the fluid medium is carried into the cell.

Since the original description of pinocytosis as merely a process of cell drinking, the concept has been revised. It has been found that protein binding at the surface of the cell is also a major factor in this process. Pinocytosis is now considered to be a form of active cell transport whereby fluid and macromolecules (proteins, polypeptides, hormones, and glucose) are incorporated into the cytoplasm of cells. At least one energy-consuming chemical reaction occurs during pinocytosis; therefore, the process is a form of active cell transport. Substances are bound to the plasma membrane; vesicles or vacuoles are formed from the plasma membrane; the vesicles invaginate the cytoplasm and are pinched off; and the substance is incorporated into the cell cyto-

plasm (Figs. 35 to 38). The dimensions of pinocytotic vesicles vary from 1 to 2 microns in ameba to 10 millimicrons in intestinal epithelial cells. Regardless of the size of the droplet and the mechanism of incorporation into the cell, the basic process of pinocytosis is the same, a drop of fluid is surrounded by plasma membrane and subsequently moved into the interior of the cell.

Pinocytosis occurs in many cells, including amebas, leukocytes, intestinal and renal epithelial cells, reticuloendothelial cells, some malignant and benign tissue culture cells, some plant root cells, and many cells of the embryo (Figs. 36 to 38). Transendothelial passage of minute quantities (*quanta transport*) of solutes and water in capillaries occurs by pinocytosis (Figs. 36 and 39).

Pinocytosis can be induced by certain sub-

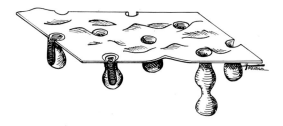

Fig. 35. Three-dimensional schematic representation of pinocytotic vesicles (*caveolae intracellulares*) formed from the plasma membrane.

31

Fig. 36.

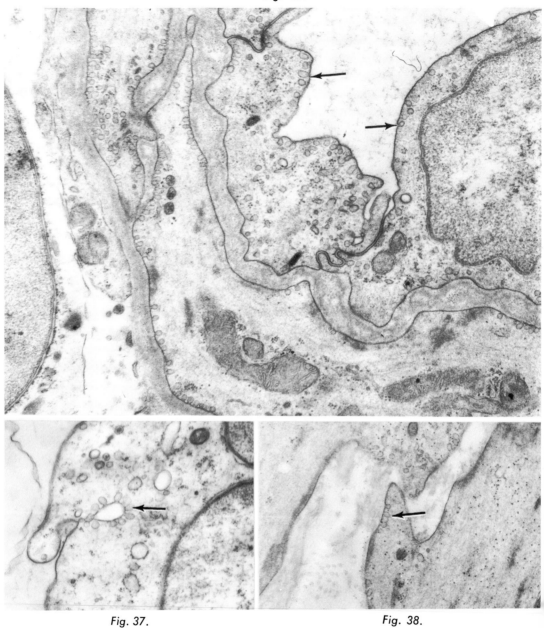

Fig. 37.   Fig. 38.

Fig. 36. Pinocytotic vesicles in vascular endothelium (arrows). Rat liver arteriole. × 36,000.

Fig. 37. Cells grown in tissue culture with pinocytotic vesicles (arrow). Human cartilage cell 48 hours in vitro tissue culture. × 25,000.

Fig. 38. Smooth muscle cell with numerous pinocytotic vesicles (arrows). Dog aorta. × 21,000.

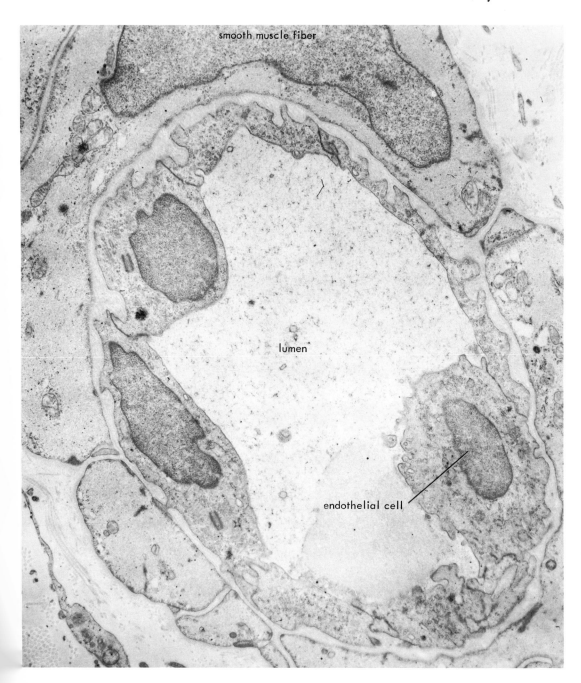

Fig. 39. Numerous pinocytotic vesicles are characteristic of endothelium of "muscle type" capillary (as opposed to "fenestrated" and "sinusoidal types" of capillaries). There may be as many as 120 to 140 vesicles per square micron of endothelium, representing about one third of endothelial cell volume. Arteriole of dog esophagus. × 15,000.

stances in the extracellular medium, such as gamma globulin, gelatin, insulin, lysozyme, amino acids, viruses, toluidine blue, and the cations magnesium, potassium, and sodium. Moreover, neither carbohydrate nor nucleic acid can induce the process. The temperature and pH of the medium and factors concerned with the electrical charge of the plasma membrane affect pinocytosis.

There are many factors in the process of pinocytosis that remain to be determined. How is the material bound, and what physical and chemical changes occur in the plasma membrane in this process? Almost certainly there is rapid formation of new membrane to replace that utilized to surround the vacuole. Is the pinocytotic membrane continuous with the endoplasmic reticulum? Can these vacuoles become lysosomes? The answers to these questions are not yet known.

REFERENCES

BENNETT, H.: The concepts of membrane flow and membrane vesiculation as mechanisms for active transport and ion pumping. J. Biophys. Biochem. Cytol., Suppl., 2:99–103, 1956.

EASTON, J., B. GOLDBERG, and H. GREEN: Demonstration of surface antigens and pinocytosis in mammalian cells with ferritin-antibody conjugates. J. Cell Biol., 12:437–443, 1962.

FAWCETT, D.: Comparative observations on the fine structure of blood capillaries, in *The Peripheral Blood Vessels*, edited by J. Orbison and D. Smith, pp. 17–44. The Williams and Wilkins Company, Baltimore, 1963.

HOLTER, H.: Pinocytosis, in *Biological Structure and Function*, vol. I, edited by T. Goodwin and O. Lindberg, pp. 157–168. Academic Press, Inc., New York, 1961.

LEWIS, W.: Pinocytosis. Johns Hopkins Hosp. Med. Bull., 49:17–28, 1931.

PALADE, G.: Blood capillaries of the heart and other organs. Circulation, 24:368–384, 1961.

RUSTAD, R.: Pinocytosis. Sci. Amer., 204:120–130, 1961.

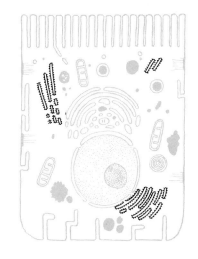

5

ENDOPLASMIC RETICULUM AND ERGASTOPLASM

The portion of the cytoplasm that stains with basic dyes was designated *ergastoplasm* by Garnier in 1897, and was largely forgotten until "rediscovered" by electron microscopists. Using the electron microscope Porter, in 1945, described a number of intracytoplasmic membrane systems, including the ergastoplasm, which he collectively named *endoplasmic reticulum*. Ergastoplasm is generally considered today as that part of the endoplasmic reticulum that has two characteristic components: (1) networks of canaliculi, flattened sacs, vacuoles, or cisternae that have a limiting membrane 40 to 60 Ångstroms thick, and (2) regularly placed dense granules of ribonucleoprotein (ribosomes or RNA), about 150 Ångstroms in diameter, along the outer surface of the membranes. The ergastoplasm is commonly called rough-surfaced endoplasmic reticulum (Figs. 40 and 41). In contrast to this, there is a smooth-surfaced reticulum that has no granular component along the membrane (Figs. 42 and 43). A specialized form of smooth-surfaced endoplasmic reticulum is represented by the Golgi complex (Figs. 44 and 47 to 51).

When the endoplasmic reticulum was "rediscovered" by electron microscopists a great deal was known about its metabolism and chemistry. For a number of years cytochemists had studied a cell component called the *microsomal fraction*, obtained by fractionating cells and centrifuging the disrupted cells at high speed. The nucleus, being the largest and heaviest cell component, was centrifuged out first; with higher speed centrifugation the mitochondria were centrifuged out; and with still greater speed a microsomal fraction was obtained. The microsomal fraction was shown by Palade to be the ergastoplasm; thus chemistry and morphology were wedded. Combined chemical and morphological studies by Palade and Siekevitz and others have yielded a great deal of information about the function of the various forms of the endoplasmic reticulum.

The type (smooth-surfaced or rough-surfaced) of endoplasmic reticulum and the morphologic form (sacs, vacuoles, cisternae, or tubes) vary with cell types and metabolic activity. Endoplasmic reticulum varies from small tubes 50 to 100 Ångstroms in diameter to large sacs several microns in diameter. The reticulum may appear rather haphazardly arranged in the cytoplasm or as neatly arrayed membrane systems (Figs. 41 and 43). The rough-surfaced endoplasmic reticulum forms the outer nuclear membrane; the nucleus and its inner membrane may be thought of as sitting in a large vacuole of rough-surfaced endoplasmic reticulum (Fig. 87). Communications have been demonstrated between the rough- and smooth-surfaced endoplasmic reticulum,

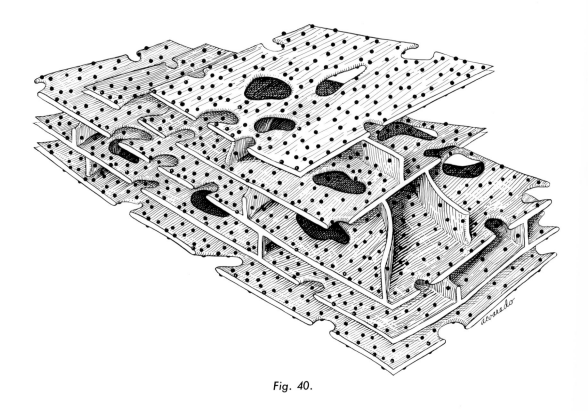

Fig. 40.

Fig. 40. Three dimensional schematic representation of ergastoplasm (rough-surfaced endoplasmic reticulum). The parallel lamellar sacs are studded with ribosomes (*Palade granules*) creating the "rough-surfaced" appearance.

Fig. 41. Regular array of ergastoplasm characteristic of cells capable of protein synthesis. Dog pancreatic acinar cell. $\times$ 35,000.

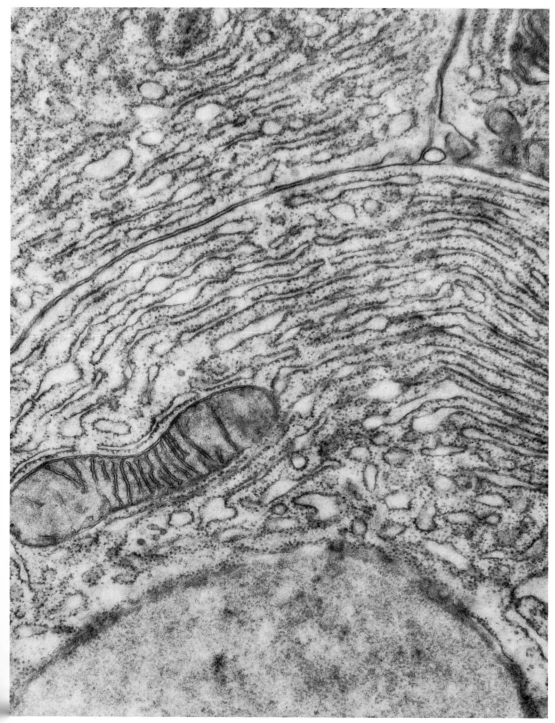

Fig. 41.

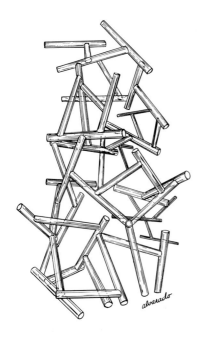

Fig. 42. Three dimensional schematic representation of the tubular form of smooth-surfaced endoplasmic reticulum, such as that found in blood monocytes and gastric parietal cells. (Redrawn from concepts presented in a Model of the Cell, The Upjohn Company, Kalamazoo, Michigan.)

Fig. 43. Smooth-surfaced endoplasmic reticulum. Cell of interstitial tissue of rat testis. × 18,000.

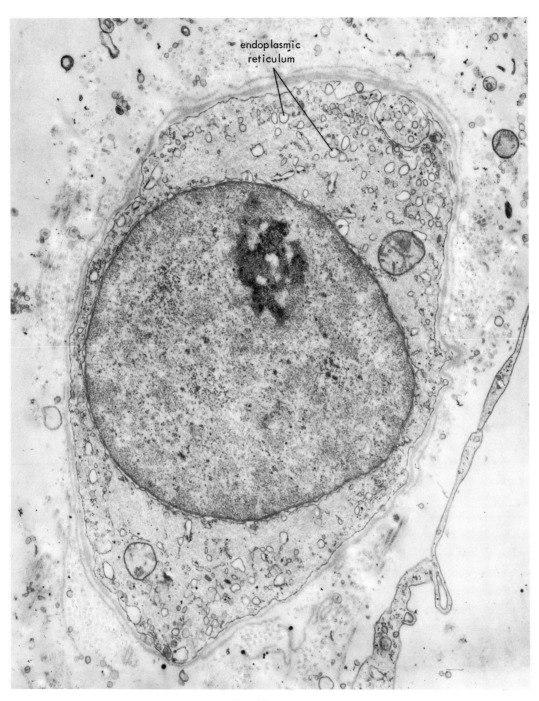

Fig. 43.

especially the smooth-surfaced reticulum comprising the Golgi complex, and continuity between the endoplasmic reticulum and the plasma membrane is suspected. It has been suggested that the endoplasmic reticulum is analagous to the digestive tract of an animal through which substances may pass, but in a geometric sense, remain outside the organism.

The ergastoplasm (microsomal cell fraction) contains protein, ribose nucleic acid, and phospholipid. The particles (ribosomes) contain nearly all the ribose nucleic acid and about 20 percent of the protein; the membranes contain nearly all the phospholipid and the balance of the protein.

The amount of endoplasmic reticulum in a cell is proportional to the capacity of the cell to synthesize new material. Protein synthesis in the endoplasmic reticulum ceases when the microsomal fraction is treated with ribonuclease, demonstrating that the ribonucleoprotein particle (ribosome) is involved with protein synthesis. However, the association of the ribosome with the membrane of the endoplasmic reticulum is not necessary for protein synthesis (Fig. 46). It has been postulated that those ribosomes attached to membranes synthesize protein for export outside the cell, while those ribosomes not associated with the membranes synthesize protein for internal use by the cell. The smooth-surfaced endoplasmic reticulum can synthesize hormones, and the association of this form of endoplasmic reticulum with glycogen suggests either an anabolic or catabolic, or both, role with glycogen. The peculiar disposition of the smooth-surfaced form of endoplasmic reticulum in striated muscle has led many investigators to suspect that this membrane system is involved in the intracellular transmission of nerve impulses (Fig. 45). In the exocrine cells of the pancreas, enzyme precursors are formed in the sacs of the rough-surfaced endoplasmic reticulum. It is thought that many substances synthesized by the ergastoplasm are transported to the Golgi complex where they are concentrated into granules or droplets. Such a secretory process has been suggested for the formation of zymogen granules of pancreatic exocrine cells, mucin droplets of the intestinal goblet cells, hormones of cells of the anterior pituitary, and many others (Figs. 50 to 52 and 56 to 59).

REFERENCES

HAGUENAU, F.: The ergastoplasm; its history, ultrastructure and biochemistry. Intern. Rev. Cytol., 7:425–483, 1958.

KUROSUMI, K.: Electron miscroscopic analysis of the secretion mechanism. Intern. Rev. Cytol., 11:1–124, 1961.

PALADE, G., and K. PORTER: Studies on the endoplasmic reticulum. 1. Its identification in cells in situ. J. Exper. Med., 100:641–656, 1954.

PALADE, G., and P. SIEKEVITZ: Liver microsomes: An integrated morphological and biochemical study. J. Biophys. Biochem. Cytol., 2:671–690, 1956.

PALADE, G.: A small particulate component of the cytoplasm, in *Frontiers in Cytology*, edited by S. Palay, pp. 283–304. Yale University Press, New Haven, 1958.

PORTER, K.: Electron microscopy of basophilic components of cytoplasm. J. Histochem. Cytochem., 2:346–373, 1954.

PORTER, K.: The sarcoplasmic reticulum. Its recent history and present status. J. Biophys. Biochem. Cytol., Suppl., 10:219–226, 1961.

RUSKA, H., G. EDWARDS, and R. CAESAR: A concept of intracellular transmission of excitation by means of endoplasmic reticulum. Experentia, 14:117–120, 1958.

SIEKEVITZ, P., and G. PALADE: A cytochemical study on the pancreas of the guinea pig. VI. Release of enzymes and ribonucleic acid from ribonucleoprotein particles. J. Biophys. Biochem. Cytol., 7:631–644, 1960.

WEISS, J.: The ergastoplasm: Its fine structure and relation to protein synthesis as studied with the electron microscope in the pancreas of the Swiss albino mouse. J. Exper. Med., 98:607–618, 1953.

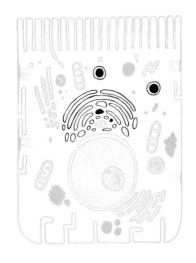

6

GOLGI COMPLEX AND SECRETORY PRODUCTS

Golgi in 1898 described a structure in the cytoplasm of nerve cells that has since become known as the *Golgi complex*. Almost since its discovery the Golgi complex has been subject of controversy, and until recent years, some considered it an artifact. Studies using density-gradient ultracentrifugation, phase microscopy, and especially the electron microscopic studies of Dalton and Felix, have demonstrated a Golgi complex in the cytoplasm of all cells investigated in both the animal and plant kingdoms. In animal cells, it may be called the Golgi complex, zone, substance, or material; in plant cells it is called the *dictyosome*.

In light microscopy, the Golgi complex is defined by its capacity to react with silver salts or osmium tetroxide. It is difficult to recognize by phase microscopy, however, because it has a refractive index very similar to that of cytoplasm in general. With electron microscopic techniques using silver or osmium impregnation, the Golgi complex varies in amount and organization depending on the type and functional state of the cell (Fig. 140). It appears as dense anastomosing cords, vacuoles with clear centers and dense peripheries, or as an irregular fenestrated plate. In general, the Golgi complex is large in metabolically active cells and small in resting and old cells. The position of the Golgi complex

in the cell depends on the cell type, but in most cells it is located in a supranuclear position partially enclosing the centrosome or cell center (Fig. 48).

In electron microscopy the Golgi complex has a distinctive structure; it appears as ordered arrays of parallel membranes about 60 to 70 Ångstroms thick consisting of flattened sacs usually displayed in a crescentic arrangement (Figs. 47 to 51). Associated with the flattened sacs are small vesicles and vacuoles of varying size limited by smooth membranes. In some cells the vacuoles may contain electron-dense granules (Fig. 50). The smooth-surfaced membranes of the Golgi material are continuous with the rough-surfaced membranes of the endoplasmic reticulum and the Golgi complex is actually a specialized form of smooth-surfaced endoplasmic reticulum.

Chemical analysis of Golgi material isolated by density-gradient ultracentrifugation has revealed it to be principally phospholipid. There is a high level of acid phosphatase activity and lesser levels of alkaline phosphatase and other enzymes.

The Golgi complex is involved somehow in cellular import and export activities and on the basis of morphologic evidence, it has been suggested that the Golgi complex serves as a site for the concentration of materials produced at other locations in the cell. The par-

Fig. 44. Rough-surfaced endoplasmic reticulum (*ergastoplasm*) and smooth-surfaced membranes of Golgi complex can be compared in this micrograph. Guinea pig salivary gland acinar cell. $\times$ 34,000.

Fig. 45. Striated muscle filaments showing network of smooth-surfaced endoplasmic reticulum. Rat cardiac muscle. $\times$ 30,000.

Fig. 46. Cytoplasm of motor neuron with ribosomes not associated with membranes of endoplasmic reticulum. Dog cerebral cortex. $\times$ 27,000.

Fig. 44.

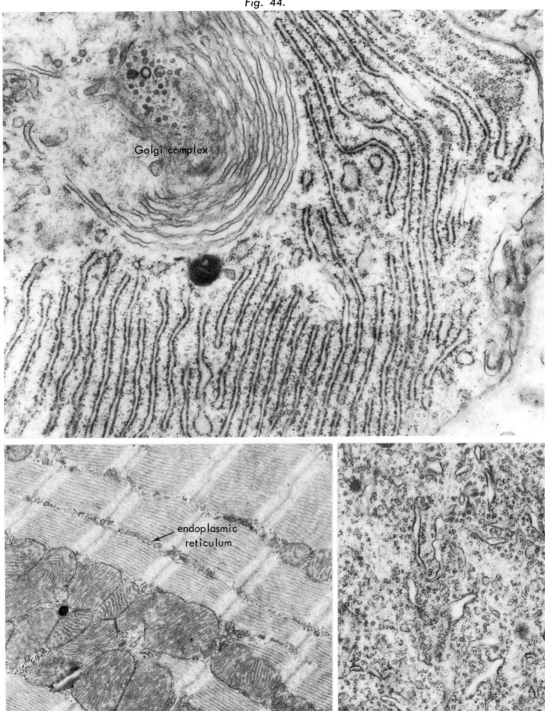

Fig. 45.

Fig. 46.

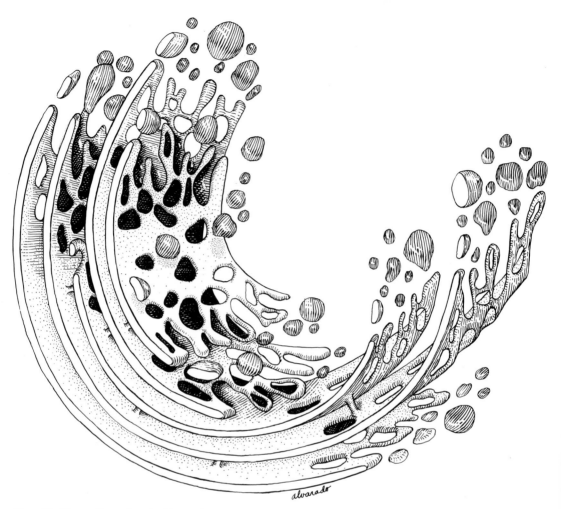

Fig. 47. Three-dimensional schematic representation of Golgi complex, which consists of ordered arrays of parallel sacs and vesicles of the smooth-surfaced form of the intracytoplasmic (endoplasmic) reticular system.

Fig. 48. Golgi complex with a centriole. Human bone marrow, neutrophilic myelocyte. × 20,000.

Fig. 49. Membranes of Golgi complex. Rat epididymis. × 30,000.

Fig. 48.

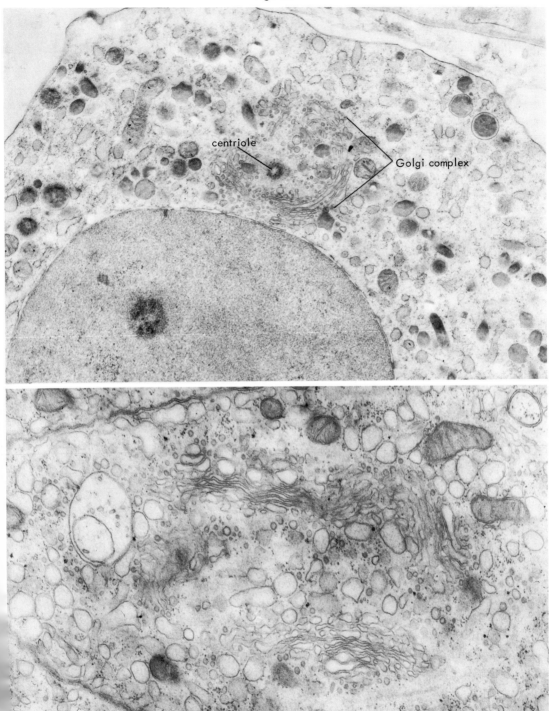

Fig. 49.

Fig. 50.

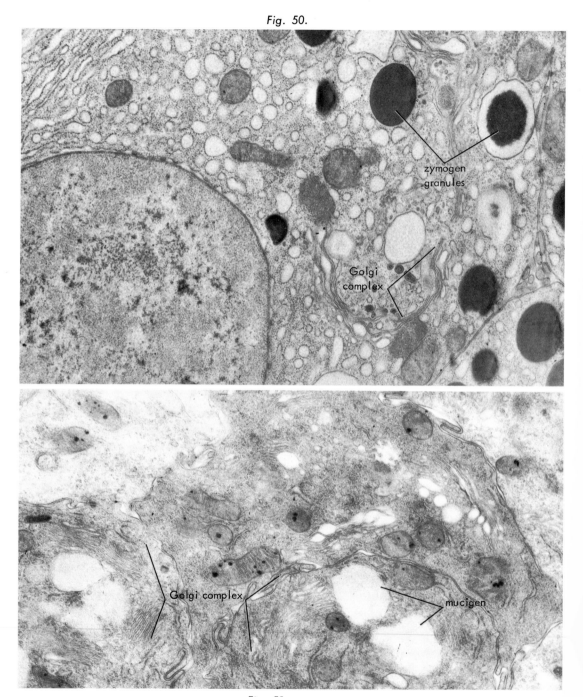

Fig. 51.

Fig. 50. Golgi complex. Dog pancreatic acinar cells. Note the zymogen granules. × 13,000.

Fig. 51. Proliferated Golgi complex containing mucigen in goblet cells. Rat ileum. × 25,000.

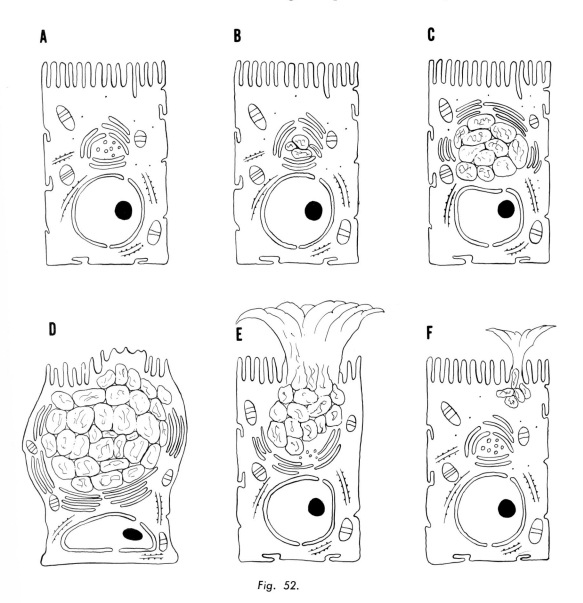

Fig. 52.

Fig. 52. Two-dimensional schematic representation of the participation of Golgi complex in formation of mucous in a goblet cell. The first visible droplets of mucigen form in Golgi vesicles (*A, B*); the Golgi membranes proliferate (*C*); droplets coalesce into mucin (*D*); and the mucin is forced to the surface of the cell, rupturing the plasma membrane (*E, F*). (Redrawn and modified from J. Freeman, Anat. Rec., **144**:343, 1962).

Fig. 53.

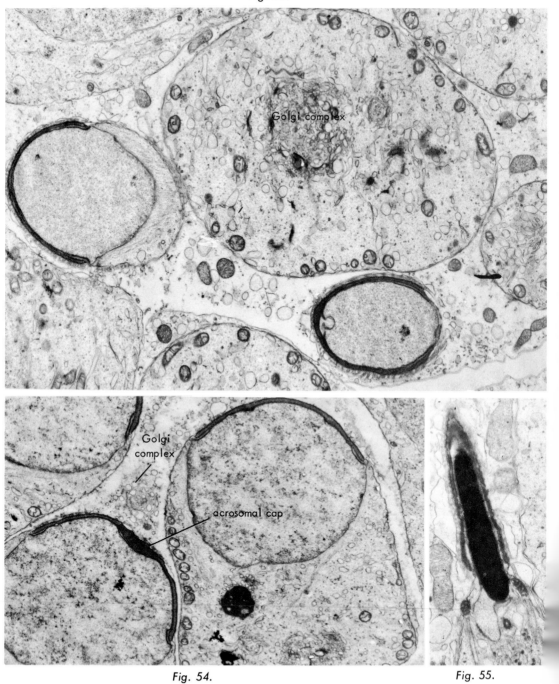

Fig. 53. Golgi complex. Spermatogonium of rat testis. $\times$ 15,000.

Fig. 54. Formation of acrosomal cap by Golgi complex. Rat testis. $\times$ 7,500.

Fig. 55. Fully formed acrosome of spermatid. Rat testis. $\times$ 11,000.

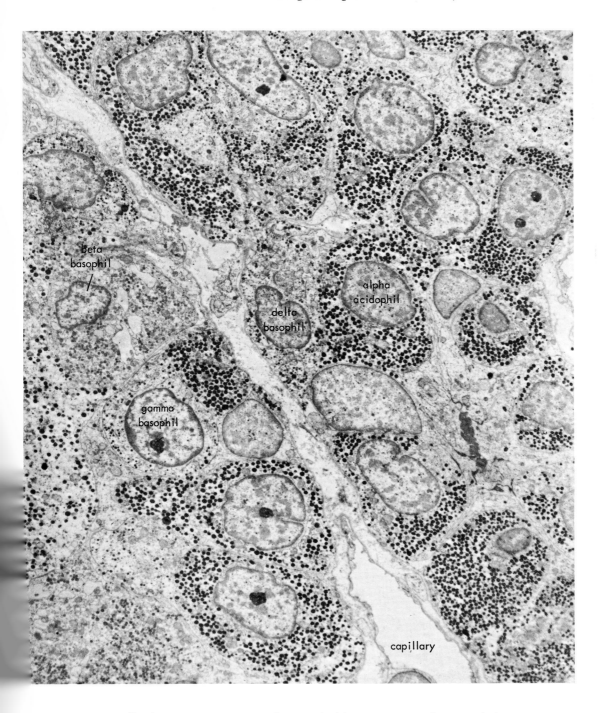

Fig. 56. Cells of anterior pituitary are distinguished by staining reaction, morphology, and functional changes under experimental conditions. The cells currently are divided into six types—alpha and epsilon acidophils; beta, gamma, and delta basophils; and chromophobes. Dog. $\times$ 4,100.

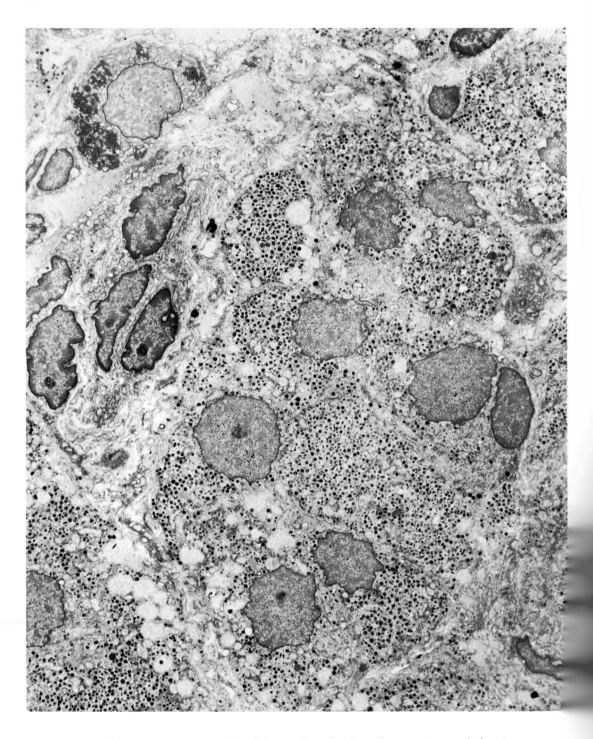

Fig. 57. Neurosecretory granules of chromaffin cells. Granules contain catechol amines (epinephrine and norepinephrine). Because of their minute size, granules are not visible with the light microscope as are the granules of cells of anterior pituitary. Cat adrenal medulla. × 4,100.

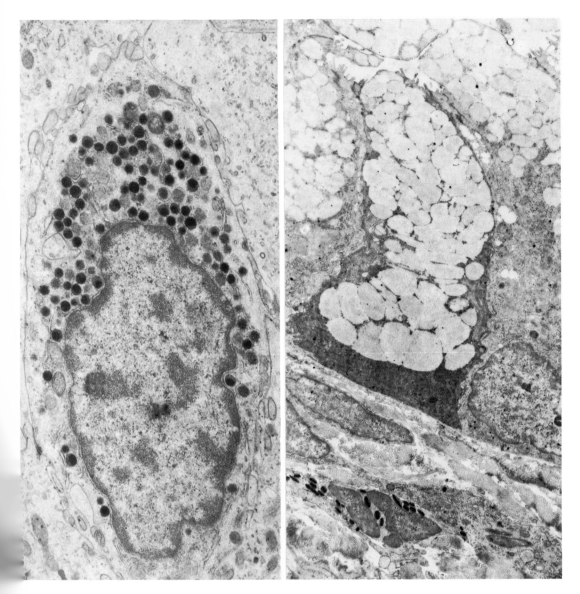

Fig. 58.   Fig. 59.

Fig. 58. Argentaffine cell. Secretory granules vary in size and structure. Rat ileum. × 15,000.

Fig. 59. Mucous secretion in goblet cells. Compare this type of secretion with granule secretion of Fig. 56 to 58. Rat ileum. × 5,600. (Reproduced from J. Freeman, Anat. Rec., **144**:347, 1962.)

ticipation of the Golgi complex in the formation of zymogen granules in the pancreatic exocrine cell was described with the endoplasmic reticulum (Fig. 50). The Golgi complex is involved in the formation of catechol amines (epinephrine and norepinephrine) in the cells of the adrenal medulla, of secretory granules in the anterior pituitary, and of mucin in the intestinal goblet cells (Figs. 56, 57, and 59).

The Golgi complex is active in the production of acrosomal granules of spermatids (Figs. 53 to 55) and plays an important role in the intestinal absorption of lipids. It still is not known why the Golgi complex is so highly developed in nerve cells.

REFERENCES

BARNES, B.: Electron microscope studies on the secretory cytology of the mouse anterior pituitary. Endocrin. **71**:618–628, 1962.

BURGOS, M., and D. FAWCETT: Studies on the fine structure of the mammalian testis. I. Differentiation of the spermatids in the cat (*Felis domesticas*). J. Biophys. Bichem. Cytol., **1**: 287–300, 1955.

CARO, L.: Electron microscopic radioautography of thin sections: The Golgi zone as a site of protein concentration in pancreatic acinar cells. J. Biophys. Biochem. Cytol., **10**:37–45, 1961.

CLERMONT, Y.: The Golgi zone of the rat spermatid and its role in the formation of cytoplasmic vesicles. J. Biophys. Biochem. Cytol., Suppl., **2**:119–122, 1956.

DALTON, A., and M. FELIX: A comparative study of the Golgi complex. J. Biophys. Biochem. Cytol., Suppl., **2**:79–84, 1956.

DALTON, A.: Golgi apparatus and secretion granules, in *The Cell*, vol. II, edited by J. Brachet and A. Mirsky, pp. 603–619. Academic Press, Inc., New York, 1961.

FREEMAN, J.: Fine structure of the goblet cell mucous secretory process. Anat. Rec., **144**:341–358, 1962.

KUROSUMI, K.: Electron microscopic analysis of the secretion mechanism. Intern. Rev. Cytol., **11**:1–124, 1961.

LEVER, J.: Fine structural organization in endocrine tissue. Brit. Med. Bull., **18**:229–232, 1962.

POLLISTER, A., and P. POLLISTER: The structure of the Golgi apparatus. Intern. Rev. Cytol., **6**:85–106, 1957.

WEISS, J.: The role of the Golgi complex in fat absorption as studied with the electron microscope with observations on the cytology of the duodenal absorptive cells. J. Exper. Med., **102**:775–781, 1955.

ZEIGEL, R., and A. DALTON: Speculations based on the morphology of the Golgi systems in several types of protein-secreting cells. J. Cell Biol., **15**:45–54, 1962.

ZELANDER, T.: Ultrastructure of mouse adrenal cortex. An electron microscopical study in intact and hydrocortisome treated male adults. J. Ultrast. Res., Suppl. 2, 1959.

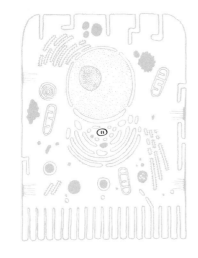

7 CENTRIOLES

Close to the nucleus and usually near the geometric center of the cell is a condensed portion of the cytoplasm (*cell center* or *centrosome*). In the centrosome there may be seen a single granule (*centriole*) or two such granules (*diplosome*) surrounded by a clear zone which in turn is surrounded by a dense zone of Golgi material. The centriole may be observed in living cells by phase microscopy, especially in the interphase of mitosis.

Using the electron microscope two centrioles can be observed in the region of the Golgi complex (Figs. 39, 48, 61, and 63). Each centriole is a cylinder approximately 500 millimicrons long and 150 millimicrons in diameter (Figs. 39 and 62). The long axis of one centriole is often at right angles to the long axis of the other centriole (Fig. 64). The wall of the centriole is composed of an electron dense material containing nine smaller cylinders arranged symmetrically with their long axes parallel to the long axis of the centriole itself (Figs. 60 and 63). Each smaller cylinder is about 150 to 200 Ångstroms in diameter, and the central portion is less dense than the surrounding matrix (Fig. 63). There is no limiting membrane about the centriole. In blood leukocytes, two *pericentriolar structures* or *satellites* have been observed outside each of the nine smaller cylinders. These satellites are dense spherical masses about 700 Ångstroms

in diameter, and they are attached at right angles to each cylinder by short "arms."

During cell division the centrioles migrate

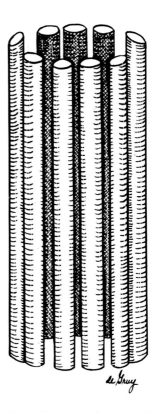

Fig. 60. Three-dimensional schematic representation of the nine cylinders of a centriole.

Fig. 61. Cross section of a centriole in Golgi complex. Human bone marrow, neutrophilic myelocyte. $\times$ 15,000.

Fig. 62. Longitudinal section of centriole in monocyte. Human bone marrow, acute monocytic leukemia. $\times$ 23,000.

Fig. 63. High magnification of longitudinally oriented cylinders of the centriole of lymphoblast. Human bone marrow, chronic lymphocytic leukemia. $\times$ 53,000.

Fig. 64. Diplosome in epithelial cell of rabbit ciliary body. One centriole has formed a rudimentary cilium. $\times$ 23,000.

Fig. 61.

Fig. 62.

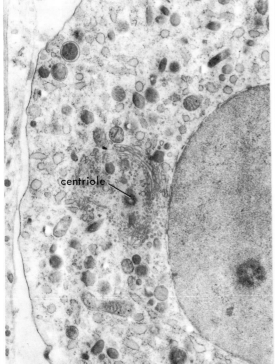

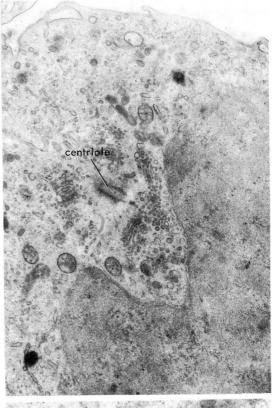

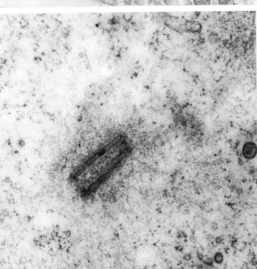

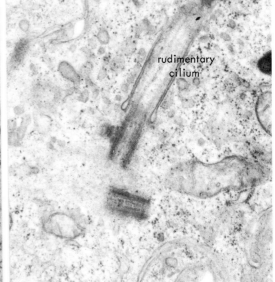

Fig. 63.

Fig. 64.

to opposite poles of the cell and form the focal points of the asters of the mitotic spindle (Fig. 88). Bessis suggests that the aster rays attach to the satellites of the centrioles. Morphologically the centriole, the basal body of cilia, and the basal body of flagella of spermatozoa have a similar filament structure (Figs. 24 and 26). The significance of this point of morphology in the evolution and function of these structures is not known.

REFERENCES

AMANO, S.: The structure of the centrioles and spindle body as observed under the electron and phase contrast microscopes. A new extension-fiber theory concerning mitotic mechanism in animal cells. Cytologia, 22:193–212, 1957.

BERNHARD, W., and E. de HARVEN: L'ultrastructure du centriole et d'autres éléments de l'appareil achromatique, in *IV International Conference on Electron Microscopy, Berlin*, Sept. 10–17, 1958, pp. 217–227. Springer-Verlag, Berlin, 1960.

BESSIS, M., J. BRETON-GORIUS, and J. THIÉRY: Centriole, corps de Golgi et aster des leucocytes. Étude au microscope électronique. Rev. Hématol., 13:363–386, 1958.

de HARVEN, E., and W. BERNHARD: Étude au microscope électronique de l'ultrastructure du centriole chez les vertébrés. Ztschr. Zellforsch., 45:375–398, 1956.

YAMADA, E.: Some observations on the fine structure of centrioles in the mitotic cell. Kurume Med. J., 5:36–38, 1958.

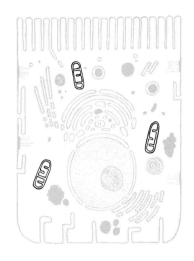

8

MITOCHONDRIA

Mitochondria are cytoplasmic organelles found in all animal cells capable of aerobic metabolism. Essentially, they are biochemical factories that function to convert chemical energy (stored adenosine triphosphate—"energy-rich phosphate bonds") into a form the cell can utilize for its metabolic activities, such as enzyme synthesis and muscle contraction.

Knowledge of both the structure and function of mitochondria was well advanced before the electron microscope was introduced. Mitochondria had been observed in living cells by phase microscopy and were demonstrated by supravital stains such as Janus green B and neutral red. Mitochondria in the living cell may swell, contract, elongate, shorten, or fragment; they may be spherical, rod shaped, or filamentous. Swelling can be inhibited by respiratory enzyme inhibitors (such as potassium cyanide and amytal).

By use of the electron microscope Palade and Sjöstrand have described the mitochondrion as an ovoid or elongate structure that is limited externally by a double membrane (Figs. 65, 66, and 68). The outer and inner membranes measure 40 to 60 Ångstroms in thickness and are separated by a space of low electron density about 100 Ångstroms in thickness (Fig. 68). Each membrane has a basic trilaminar unit membrane structure (see

Chap. 3). There are varying numbers of internal double membranes, depending on the cell type and its metabolic activity. They radiate toward the center of an ovoid mitochondrion. In an elongate mitochondrion they lie either in the plane of the long axis as in parts of the nervous system, or perpendicular to the long axis as in the liver and kidney (Fig. 66). In endocrine tissues such as the ovary and the adrenal cortex and in the protozoa the internal membranes are tubular (Fig. 69). These internal double membranes (*cistae mitochondriales*) are continuous with the inner limiting membrane (Figs. 65 and 68). Some cristae extend from one limiting membrane to the other; and others, for only variable distances into the mitochondrial matrix. By and large, the mitochondria of a particular cell type are fairly constant in size, shape, and organization of cristae. The electron density of the mitochondrial matrix varies with the cell type. Many mitochondria contain small dense particles. High magnification of the inner mitochondrial membranes, has revealed subunits (*elementary particles*) on the membranes, which measure 75 to 80 Ångstroms in diameter on a stem 45 to 50 Ångstroms in length and 30 to 35 Ångstroms in width. On the outer membrane hollow cylinders have been observed 60 Ångstroms long and 60 Ångstroms

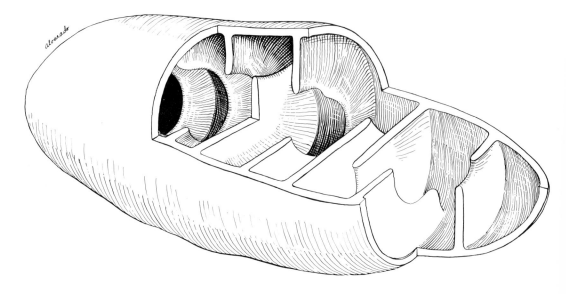

Fig. 65.

Fig. 65. Three-dimensional schematic representation of a mitochondrion with a portion of the outer membrane cut away to show internal partitions (*cristae mitochondriales*).

Fig. 66. Mitochondria. Proximal renal tubular epithelium of rat. Note the shape, size, number, and location of mitochondria in these cells. $\times$ 16,000.

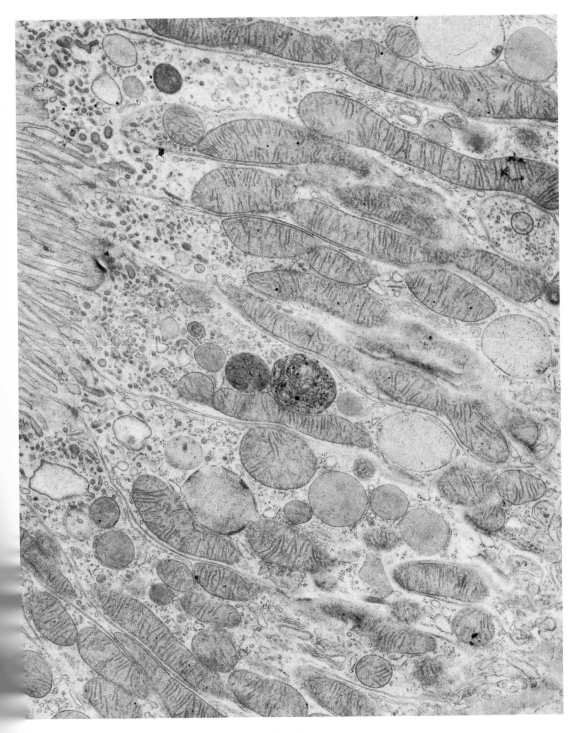

Fig. 66.

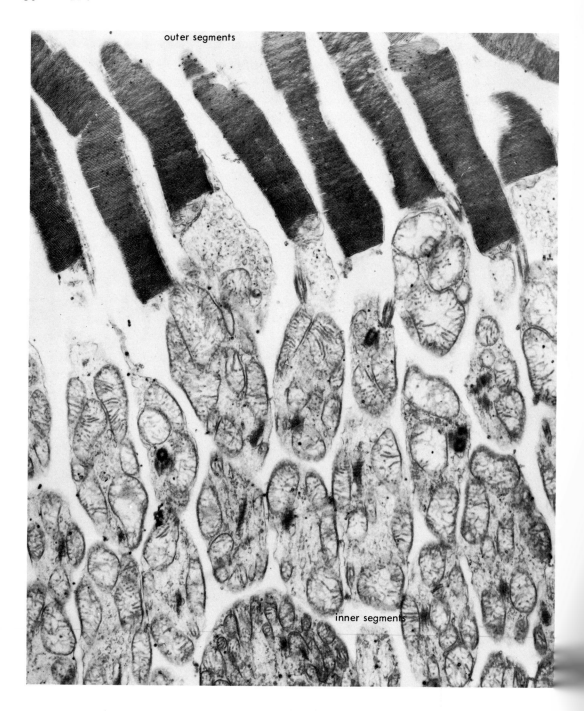

Fig. 67. The numerous mitochondria of the inner segments of retinal rods reflect the high energy requirement of the visual apparatus. Dog. $\times$ 11,000.

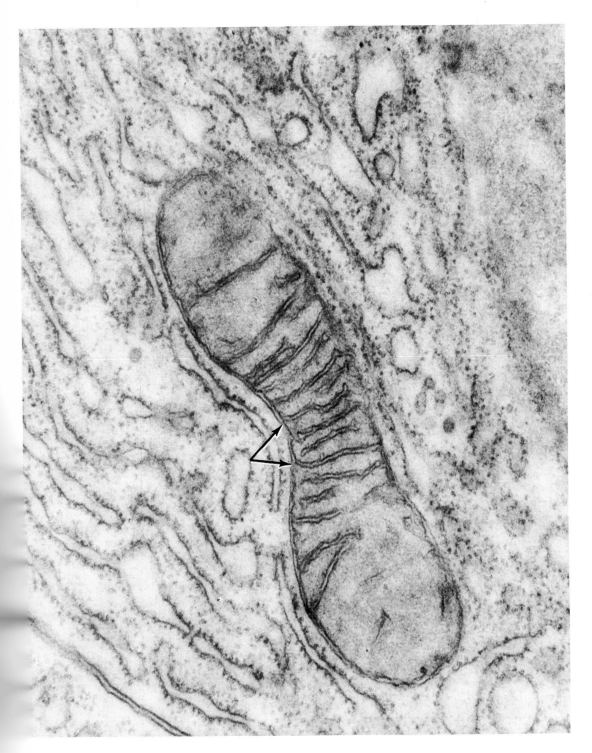

Fig. 68. Mitochondrion with cristae mitochondriales originating from internal membrane. Dog pancreatic acinar cell. × 64,000.

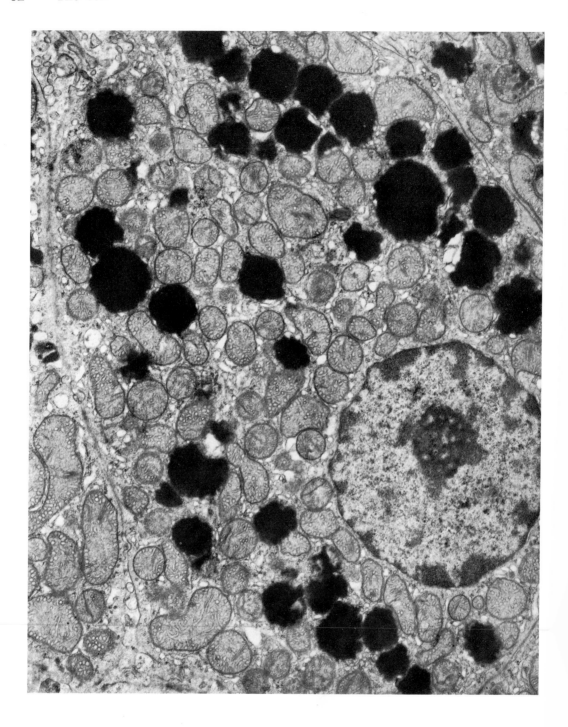

Fig. 69. Mitochondria with tubular cristae mitochondriales. In adrenal cortical cells mitochondria are associated with lipid droplets in the formation of hormones (corticoids or steroids). Cat. $\times$ 15,000.

wide. The elementary particles have been related to the electron transport (*cytochrome oxidase*) system.

Lipid inclusions are frequently associated with mitochondria in fasting or starving animals (Figs. 69 and 74). The lipid is derived from mobilization of lipid stored in fatty tissues and is not synthesized by the mitochondria. Mitochondria, as well as the cytoplasm, contain some non-heme iron, especially in erythroblasts. In diseases characterized by defective hemoglobin synthesis (thalassemia and hypochromic anemias) iron may accumulate in the mitochondria of erythroblasts.

REFERENCES

FREEMAN, J.: The ultrastructure of the double membrane systems of mitochondria. J. Biophys. Biochem. Cytol., Suppl., 2:353–354, 1956.

GANSLER, H., and C. ROUILLER: Modifications physiologiques et pathologiques du chondriome. Schweiz. Ztschr. Path. Bakt., 19:217–243, 1956.

GREEN, D.: Mitochondrial structure and function, in *Subcellular Particles*, edited by T. Hayashi, pp. 84–102. The Ronald Press, New York, 1959.

GREEN, D.: The Mitochondrion. Sci. Amer., 210: 63–74, 1964.

LANZAVECCHI, G.: L'ultrastruttura dei mitochondria in cellule di differenti organi. Rend. Sci. Istituto Lombardo, 90:536–540, 1956.

LEHNINGER, A.: How cells transform energy. Sci. Amer., 205:63–73, 1961.

LOW, F.: Mitochondrial structure. J. Biophys. Biochem. Cytol., Suppl., 2:337–340, 1956.

MOLBERT, E. and K. ARNESEN: Elektronenmikroskopische untersuchungen zur ultrastruktur der nebennierenrinde der weissen maus. (Zugleich ein beitrag zur struktur und funktion der mitochondrien). Bietr. Path. Anat. allgem. Path., 122:31–56, 1960.

NOVIKOFF, A.: Mitochondria (chondriosomes), in *The Cell*, vol. II, edited by J. Brachet and A. Mirsky, pp. 299–403. Academic Press, Inc., New York, 1961.

PALADE, G.: An electron microscopic study of the mitochondrial structure. J. Histochem. Cytochem., 1:188–211, 1953.

PARSONS, D.: Mitochondrial structure: Two types of subunits on negatively stained mitochondrial membranes. Science, 140:985–987, 1963.

SIEKEVITZ, P. and M. WATSON: Cytochemical studies of mitochondria. II. Enzymes associated with a mitochondrial membrane fraction. J. Biophys. Biochem. Cytol., 2:653–670, 1956.

SJÖSTRAND, F.: Electron microscopy of mitochondria and cytoplasmic double membranes. Nature, 171:30–32, 1953.

SJÖSTRAND, F.: Fine structure of cytoplasm: The organization of membranous layers, in *Biophysical Science—A Study Program*, edited by J. Oncley, F. Schmitt, R. Williams, M. Rosenberg, and R. Bolt, pp. 301–318. John Wiley & Sons, New York, 1959.

9

GLYCOGEN

Glycogen is a highly branched polymer of D-glucose that serves as a storage depot from which the glucose needed for the metabolic activities of the cell can be released by enzymatic degradation. It is found in many cells, but the principal body store is in liver and muscle cells (Figs. 70 and 71). Glycogen, which exists as a colloid, is soluble in aqueous fixatives and optimum preservation requires alcohol fixation. It can be demonstrated histochemically for light microscopy by the periodic acid-Schiff reaction or the iodine reaction.

Phosphate buffered osmium tetroxide preserves glycogen better for electron microscopy than does veronal buffered osmium tetroxide. In electron micrographs glycogen may appear as areas of low electron density in the cytoplasm, or as dense granules 200 to 400 Ångstroms in diameter (Fig. 72). This varying appearance is probably related to the type of glycogen polymer. Recent studies with liver cells have shown a close association between the dense granular form of glycogen and the smooth-surfaced form of endoplasmic reticulum.

REFERENCES

ANDERSON-CEDERGREN, E., and U. MUSCATELLO: The participation of the sarcotubular system in glycogen metabolism. J. Ultrast. Res., **8**:391–401, 1963.

DROCHMANS, P.: Morphologie du glycogène. Étude au microscope électronique de colorations negatives du glycogène particulaire. J. Ultrast. Res., **6**:141–163, 1962.

KARRER, H.: Electron microscopic study of glycogen in chick embryo liver. J. Ultrast. Res., **4**:191–212, 1960.

PORTER, K.: The endoplasmic reticulum: Some current interpretations of its form and functions, in *Biological Structure and Function*, vol. I., edited by T. Goodwin and O. Lindberg, pp. 127–154. Academic Press, Inc., New York, 1961.

REVEL, J., L. NAPOLITANO, and D. FAWCETT: Identification of glycogen in electron micrographs of thin tissue sections. J. Biophys. Biochem. Cytol., **8**:575–589, 1960.

Fig. 70. Unstained glycogen in a liver cell. Compare this with dense glycogen stained with lead hydroxide in Figures 71 and 72. Guinea pig. $\times$ 13,000.

Fig. 71. Granules of glycogen between muscle fibrils. Dog diaphragmatic skeletal muscle. $\times$ 10,000.

Fig. 72. Star-shaped aggregates of dense glycogen granules. Dog liver. $\times$ 30,000.

Fig. 70.

Fig. 71.

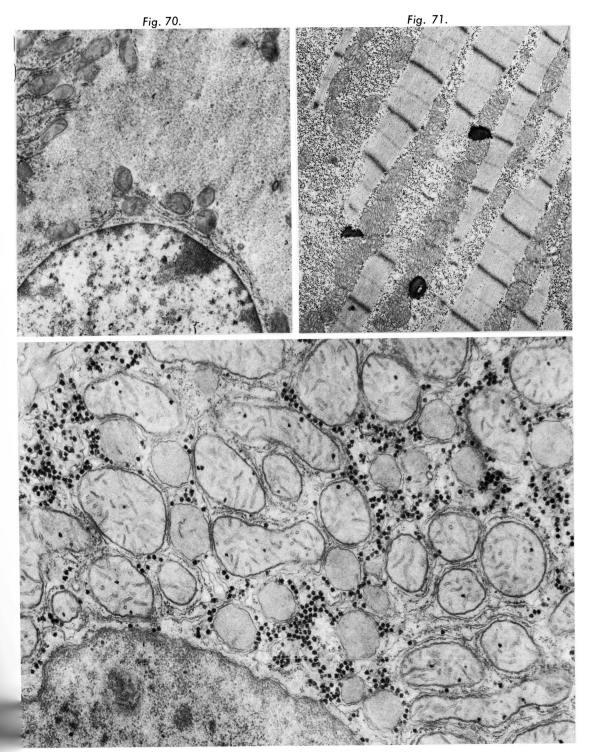

Fig. 72.

10

LIPIDS

Lipids comprise a large proportion of the mass of all cells, although usually not identifiable as such morphologically. A large proportion of the lipid in cells is masked, existing in combination with protein as lipoprotein. The lipoproteins are the basic chemical unit of nearly all, if not all of the membranes in a cell. Under certain conditions lipids may be visible as discrete inclusions in the cytoplasm and nucleus. Such inclusions can be demonstrated in light microscopy with fat stains such as Sudan III, Sudan IV, Sudan black, and oil red O.

The morphology of lipid inclusions as seen with the electron microscope depends on the class of lipid and the content of unsaturated fatty acids. Those lipids with a high content of unsaturated fatty acids readily reduce the osmium tetroxide in the fixative and thus appear dense in electron micrographs (Figs. 69, 74, and 75). Conversely, those lipids containing few unsaturated fatty acids reduce little osmium tetroxide during fixation. A lipid that has not reacted with osmium tetroxide or has reacted to a limited degree will be dissolved during tissue processing, leaving a clear space in the cell (Fig. 73). The most frequently encountered lipid inclusion in electron micrographs is a dense homogeneous cytoplasmic droplet with scalloped margins and no limiting membrane (Figs. 69 and 75). Certain

cells may have large numbers of lipid inclusions, *foam cells,* in the cytoplasm and lipid in these cells usually appears as clear spaces in electron micrographs. Other cells contain abundant electron dense lipid inclusions which are known to be utilized for metabolic activities (Fig. 75). Myelin figures represent another form of lipid inclusion where the lipid is in the form of phospholipid (Fig. 76).

The dense and clear lipid inclusions are composed of varying chemical combinations of protein, cholesterol, cholesterol esters, triglycerides, phospholipids, and free fatty acids. Although we can infer from present knowledge whether a given inclusion of lipids has a high or low content of unsaturated fatty acids, the morphology gives no clue to the class of chemical components of a lipid inclusion, except in the case of myelin figures.

A normal cell may accumulate lipid in the region of mitochondria during a period of relative metabolic inactivity, e.g., pancreatic acinar cells in the post-absorptive state or inactive adrenal cortical cells (Fig. 69). However lipid inclusions usually occur in pathologic conditions where they indicate cell injury. Abnormal cytoplasmic lipid may accumulate as a result of cell injury from many diverse agents such as hypoxia, heavy metals, carbon tetrachloride, inorganic phosphorus, acidosis, and bacterial toxins. The origin of

Fig. 73. Lipid inclusions with clear centers in alveolar macrophage cytoplasm. Dog lung. $\times$ 13,000.

Fig. 74. Dense lipid inclusions in cytoplasm. Dog carotid artery smooth muscle five days in vitro tissue culture. $\times$ 13,000.

Fig. 73.

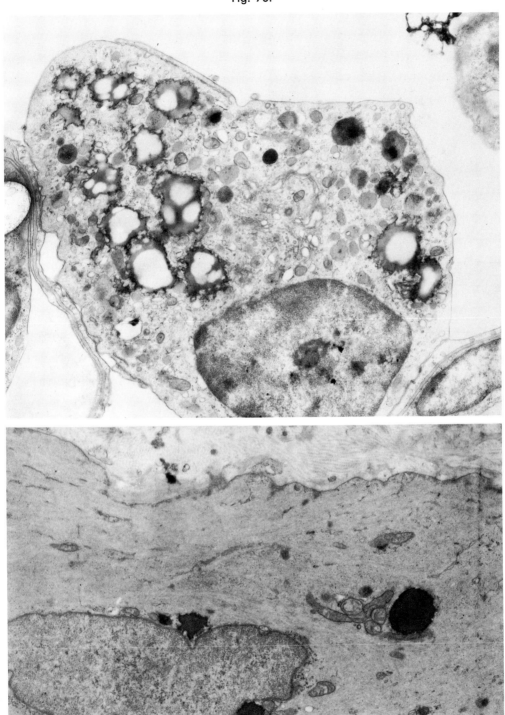

Fig. 74.

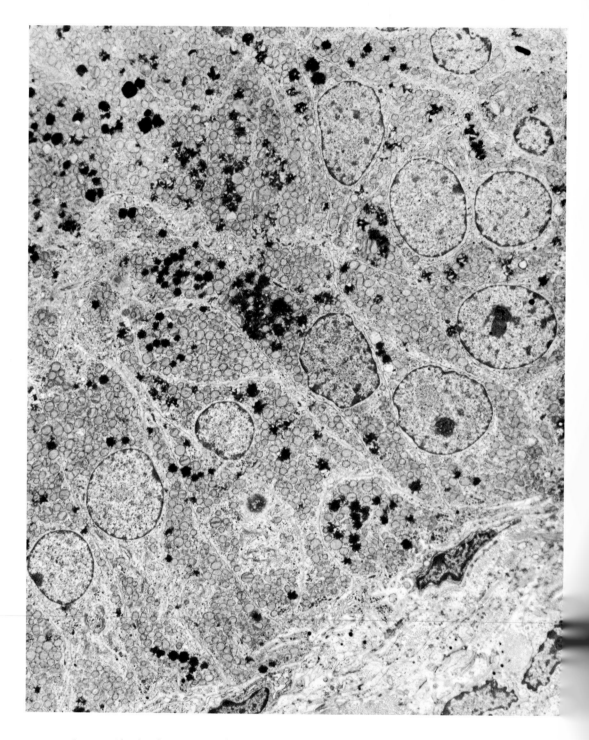

Fig. 75. The lipid content and the number of mitochondria of adrenal cortex varies with the functional activity and usually is directly proportional to secretory capacity of cells. Cat. × 4,100.

abnormal intracellular lipid has long been a subject of debate. Some have postulated the lipid inclusions result from the "unmasking" of structural lipids in the cell, i.e., releasing lipids from the lipoprotein complex of membranes. This process of unmasking has been called *phanerosis* or *fatty degeneration*. Phanerosis sometimes may account for visible cellular lipid, but in most instances the lipid has come from outside the cell.

REFERENCES

DEANE, H.: Intracellular lipids: Their detection and significance, in *Frontiers of Cytology*, edited by S. Palay, pp. 227–263. Yale University Press, New Haven, 1958.

ESSNER, E. and A. NOVIKOFF: Human hepatocellular pigments and liposomes. J. Ultrast. Res., 3:374–391, 1960.

FINEAN, J. and J. ROBERTSON: Lipids and the fine structure of myelin. Brit. Med. Bull., 14:267–273, 1958.

GEER, J., H. McGILL, JR., and J. STRONG: The fine structure of human atherosclerotic lesions. Amer. J. Path., 38:263–287, 1961.

PALADE, G.: Functional changes in structure of cell components, in *Subcellular Particles*, edited by T. Hayashi, pp. 64–80. The Ronald Press, New York, 1959.

THOENES, W.: Fine structure of lipid granules in proximal tubule cells of mouse kidney. J. Cell Biol., 12:433–437, 1962.

ZELANDER, T.: Ultrastructure of mouse adrenal cortex. An electron microscopical study in intact and hydrocortisone-treated male adults. J. Ultrast. Res., Suppl. 2, 1959.

11 MYELIN FIGURES

Myelin figures are arrays of dense membranes that may be found in the cytoplasm of cells (Fig. 76). Virchow, in 1854, first observed these structures with the penetration of water into the polar interfaces of a lipid in vitro. He coined the term *myelin*. It was later shown that these figures were bimolecular layers of lipid which alternate with layers of water. These structures superficially resemble the myelin sheath of nerves (Figs. 77 and 150).

Myelin figures are often, though not always, in the form of whorls of concentric membranes separated by an electron lucid space. They usually occur in membrane lined vacuoles in the cytoplasm (Fig. 77). A variety of other structures may also be present in these vacuoles, such as lipid droplets, ferritin particles, and other inclusions. The myelin figure may form the periphery of the entire vacuole or may be only a small inclusion at any position in the vacuole. It is possible that some of these types of cytoplasmic vacuoles are lysosomes (Fig. 76).

The presence of myelin figures in the cytoplasm is evidence of cellular degeneration, especially degeneration of the membranous components. This is not to imply inevitable cell death as this change may be localized in a small area of the cytoplasm and the cell may survive; or in some cases, the myelin figure may be the result of phagocytosis of portions of another cell that has died. Myelin figures also may be formed by changes in the protein component of the lipoprotein in cellular membranes such as the endoplasmic reticulum, plasma membranes, or mitochondria.

REFERENCES

Mercer, E.: The evolution of intracellular phospholipid membrane system, in *The Interpretation of Ultrastructure*, edited by R. Harris, pp. 369–384. Academic Press, Inc., New York, 1962.

Revel, J., S. Ito, and D. Fawcett: Electron micrographs of myelin figures of phospholipide-stimulating intracellular membranes. J. Biophys. Biochem. Cytol., 4:495–496, 1958.

Stoeckenius, W.: An electron microscope study of myelin forms. J. Biophys. Biochem. Cytol., 5:491–500, 1959.

Stoeckenius, W.: Some electron microscopical observations of liquid-crystalline phases in lipid-water systems. J. Cell Biol., 12:221–229, 1962.

Virchow, R.: Über das ausgebreitete. Vorkommen einer dem nervenmark analogen substanz in den thierischen geweben. Virchow's Arch. Path. Anat. Physiol., 6:562–572, 1854.

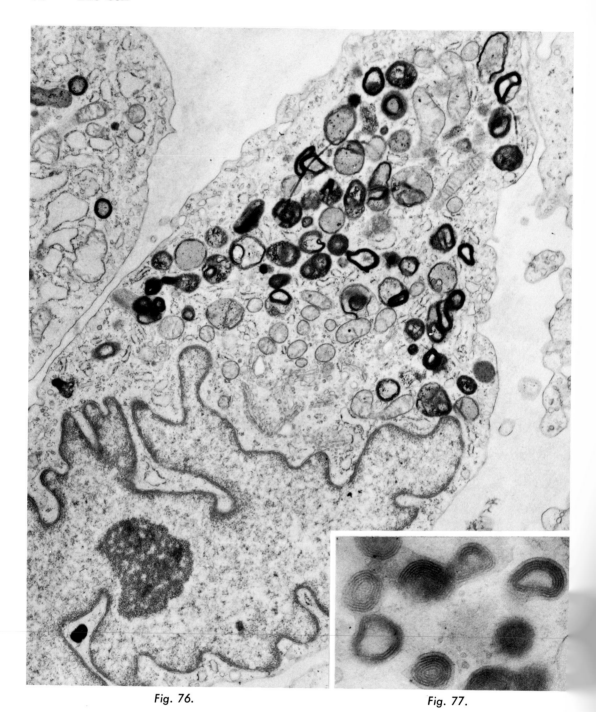

Fig. 76.   *Fig. 77.*

Fig. 76. Myelin figures in cytoplasm. Human cartilage cell forty-eight hours in vitro tissue culture. × 16,000.

Fig. 77. Kurloff bodies in lymphocyte cytoplasm appear as complex myelin figures. Guinea pig spleen. × 54,000.

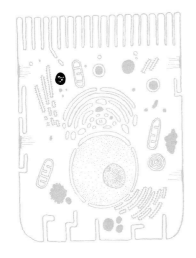

12   LYSOSOMES

The lysosome was first discovered chemically by de Duve, and only later identified morphologically. Differential centrifugation indicated the presence of a cytoplasmic particle distinct from mitochondria and microsomes that contained hydrolytic enzymes. Because of the presence of these hydrolytic enzymes these particles were named *lysosomes* (from the Greek meaning "dissolution").

Six years after the chemical discovery of lysosomes, the bodies were identified morphologically with the electron microscope. Although "dense bodies" had been observed in the cytoplasm of certain cells by electron microscopists prior to 1955, it was not until then that these bodies were identified as lysosomes. Since the lysosome did not have a constant characteristic morphology like the mitochondrion, however, positive identification required the application of histochemical techniques in electron microscopy (Figs. 78 to 81). Lysosomes are generally opaque to the electron beam. They are surrounded by a limiting membrane that serves to isolate the enzymes from the remainder of the cell, preventing digestion of the cell (Figs. 66 and 80). The matrix of the lysosome may be homogeneous and electron dense, or may contain myelin figures (*residual bodies*), or fragments of other cytoplasmic organelles (*autophagic vacuoles*) (Figs. 80 and 81). Enlarged lysosomes containing recognizable organelles such as mitochondria have been called *cytolysomes*. There is an intimate relationship of lysosomes and the Golgi complex in many cells.

Six classes of enzymes have been identified in the lysosome: phosphatases, cathepsins, glycosidases, sulfatases, ribonucleases, and deoxyribonucleases.

It is thought that lysosomes provide the enzymes for digestion of some of the materials taken into the cell by pinocytosis and phagocytosis. In conditions of starvation, on a cellular level, lysosomes probably provide the enzymes for the digestion of the cell's own cytoplasm. Similarly, when a cell dies, the lysosomal enzymes are released and digest the cell (*autolysis*).

Fig. 78. Lysosomes in proximal renal tubular epithelium of rat (arrows). $\times$ 9,200.

Fig. 79. Lysosomes with forms resembling crystals. Dog pancreatic acinar cells. $\times$ 41,000.

Fig. 80. Lysosomes containing granular material and myelin figures (residual bodies). Human cartilage cell forty-eight hours in vitro tissue culture. $\times$ 23,000.

Fig. 81. Lysosome containing lipid and fragments of cytoplasmic organelles (*autophagic vacuoles*). Dog gall bladder epithelium. $\times$ 55,000.

Fig. 78.

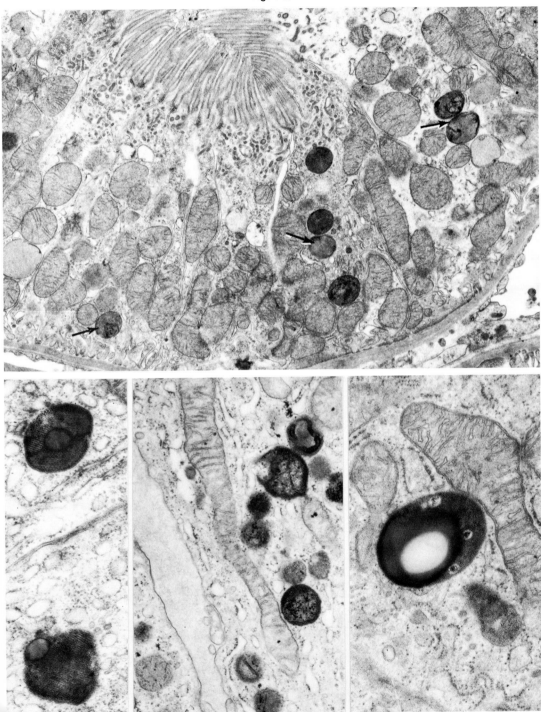

Fig. 79.

Fig. 80.

Fig. 81.

REFERENCES

Ashford, T. P., and K. R. Porter: Cytoplasmic components in hepatic cell lysosomes. J. Cell Biol., 12:198–202, 1962.

Bennett, H.: A suggestion as to the nature of the lysosome granules. J. Biophys. Biochem. Cytol., Suppl., 2:185–186, 1956.

Claude, A.: Microbodies et lysosomes: Une étude au microscope électronique. Arch. Intern. Physiol. Biochem., 68:672–673, 1960.

de Duve, C.: Lysosomes, a new group of cytoplasmic particles, in *Subcellular Particles*, edited by. T. Hayashi, pp. 128–159. The Ronald Press, New York, 1961.

de Duve, C.: The lysosome. Sci. Amer., 208:64–72, 1963.

Novikoff, A.: Lysosomes and related particles, in *The Cell*, vol. II, edited by J. Brachet and A. Mirsky, pp. 423–488. Academic Press, Inc., New York, 1961.

Novikoff, A., and E. Essner: Cytolysomes and mitochondrial degeneration. J. Cell Biol., 15:140–146, 1962.

13

PIGMENTS

MELANIN

Melanin, the major pigment of hair, feathers, the skin, the ciliary body, the iris, and part of the retina, is contained in the granules of pigment cells (*melanocytes*). These cells (Figs. 82 and 83) originate in the neural crest and migrate during embryonic development to other areas of epithelium (skin, iris, etc.).

Melanin granules are known to be relatively inert chemically. Despite over a century of study, however, the complete chemical composition of melanin pigment is not known. The pigment is formed from tyrosine by a special enzyme, tyrosinase (dopa oxydase). Melanin granules can be demonstrated in light microscopy with silver stains or the dopa reaction and the melanocytes of most vertebrates are morphologically similar. It is thought that certain connective tissue cells, especially in the dermis, can phagocytose melanin granules and appear to be pigment cells, *chromatophores*.

Viewed electron microscopically melanin granules appear as very dense round or oval structures, ranging from 0.5 to 0.8 microns in diameter, when fixed with osmium tetroxide. High magnification studies of the melanin granules show a somewhat irregular internal laminar structure and many of the granules are surrounded by a membrane (Fig. 84). The site of granule production in the cell is thought to be in the endoplasmic reticulum.

LIPOFUSCINS

Lipofuscins ("waste," atrophy pigments) are a heterogeneous group of intracellular pigments that characteristically increase in amount with the increasing age of the animal. Lipofuscins can be demonstrated in the light microscope with silver, osmium, acid-fast, sudans, periodic acid-Schiff, and other stains. Unstained lipofuscin granules are generally yellowish brown in normal visual light and give a reddish-brown fluorescence under ultraviolet light. Lipofuscins, classified on histochemical grounds, are considered to belong to the lipopigments and are suspected to be formed by the autoxidation of lipids. The different histochemical characteristics are thought to be the result of the autoxidation. Recently, cathepsin, esterase, acid phosphatase and other enzyme activities have been found in lipofuscin granules of cardiac muscle, liver, and nerve cells.

With the electron microscope the lipofuscin pigment granules appear as homogeneous aggregates of varying size, usually dense, granules (Fig. 135). The granules do not have a constant or characteristic structure and no limiting membrane is seen around any single granule. However, aggregates of granules may

Fig. 82. Pigment epithelium of anterior layer of iris with numerous melanin granules. Dog. $\times$ 8,100.

Fig. 83. Melanocyte containing numerous melanin granules. Vascular layer of dog iris. $\times$ 8,100.

Fig. 84. High magnification of melanin granules. Note irregular densities and internal laminar structure. Melanocyte of dog iris. $\times$ 23,000.

Fig. 82.

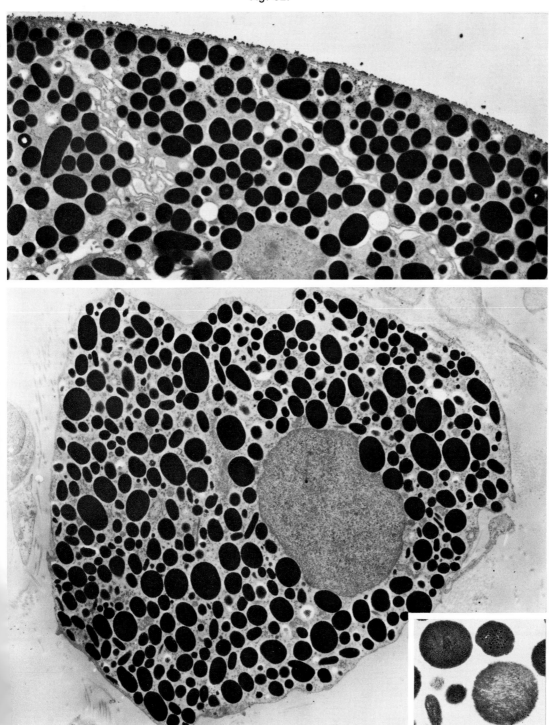

Fig. 83.

Fig. 84.

be delimited by a membrane (Fig. 135).

The intracellular site of formation of lipofuscins is not known. The Golgi complex, mitochondria, and lysosomes have been suggested as sites of formation. Because of the specific enzyme activities and the appearance of the granules in electron micrographs, current investigators consider lipofuscins to be altered lysosomes.

REFERENCES

Björkerud, S.: The isolation of lipofuscin granules from bovine cardiac muscle with observations on the properties of the isolated granules on the light and electron microscopic levels. J. Ultrast. Res., Suppl. 5, 1963.

Essner, E., and A. Novikoff: Human hepatocellular pigments and lysosomes. J. Ultrast. Res., 3:374–391, 1960.

Lillie, R.: *Histopathologic Technic and Practical Histochemistry*, pp. 248–252, McGraw-Hill Book Company, New York, 1954.

Malkoff, D., and B. Strehler: The ultrastructure of isolated and in situ human cardiac age pigment. J. Cell Biol., 16:611–616, 1963.

Moyer, F. Electron microscope observations on the origin, development, and genetic control of melanin granules in the mouse eye, in *The Structure of the Eye*, edited by G. Smelser, pp. 469–486. Academic Press, Inc., New York, 1961.

Percival, G., G. Montgomery, and T. Dodds: *Atlas of Histopathology of the Skin*, pp. 2–3, The Williams and Wilkins Company, Baltimore, 1962.

Rawles, M.: Origin of melanophores and their role in development of color patterns in vertebrates. Physiol. Rev., 28:383–408, 1948.

Selby, C.: An electron microscope study of the epidermis of mammalian skin in thin sections. J. Biophys. Biochem. Cytol., 1:429–444, 1955.

Ueno, K.: Some controversial points on the fine structure of the human iris. Kyushu J. Med. Sci., 12:43–54, 1961.

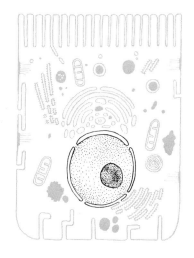

14　　　　　　　NUCLEI

The nucleus is the information center or "brain" of the cell. It is a constant component of cells, except some mature erythrocytes and thrombocytes, that varies in size, shape, and location with different cell types. In most cells the nucleus is round or ovoid in shape, but it may be irregular in contour or lobulated, and multiple nuclei may be present. The size of the nucleus is constant for a given cell type, and in general, immature cells have larger nuclei than mature cells.

With the light microscope the nucleus, with appropriate stains, is composed of an amorphous material (*nuclear sap*), filaments of chromatin, and shapely circumscribed nucleoli. The nucleus is limited by a membrane. Some bacteria, Flagellata, and Infusoria have numerous, irregular aggregates of nuclear material that are not limited by any membrane.

The appearance of the nucleus in electron microscopy depends on the fixative and on the embedding plastic. With what is generally considered good nuclear preservation, Ris has shown the nucleus to be rather homogeneous (Fig. 86). At high magnification the apparently homogeneous area contains numerous, minute filaments about 200 Ångstroms thick. The nucleolus is composed of a dense aggregate of ribosomes each measuring about 150 Ångstroms in diameter (Fig. 86). In the electron microscopic studies of Ris and Swift the

nucleus was found to be surrounded by two membranes, each about 60 Ångstroms thick, separated by a clear space approximately 120 Ångstroms wide. At intervals of about 100 millimicrons there are perforations in the double nuclear membrane (*nuclear pores*) measuring about 50 millimicrons in diameter (Figs. 85 and 87). At the site of the nuclear pores the substance of the nucleus appears to be in direct contact with the cytoplasm (Fig. 87). In some nuclei there is a single thin membrane (*diaphragm*) about 40 to 60 Ångstroms thick spanning the nuclear pores. The nuclear membrane and pores are analagous in structure to a spherical collander. The outer nuclear membrane is continuous with the ergastroplasm (rough-surfaced endoplasmic reticulum) of the cytoplasm (Fig. 87). Although the nuclear membrane fragments during the late prophase of mitosis, continuity is restored toward the end of mitosis (Fig. 88).

Chemical analysis of isolated nuclei show them to be composed of nucleohistone, deoxyribose nucleic acid, ribose nucleic acid, and alkaline phosphatase. Deoxyribose nucleic acid might be considered the "computer" of the cell, for encoded into it, specifically, in the fractions of adenine, guanine, thymine, and cytosine are the physical and chemical characteristics of the individual cell and of the

85

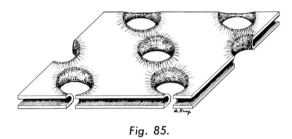

Fig. 85.

Fig. 85. Three-dimensional schematic representation of pores of nuclear membrane. Diaphragm of pores is not indicated.

Fig. 86. Cell nucleus with nucleolus. Dog sympathetic ganglion cell. $\times$ 6,400.

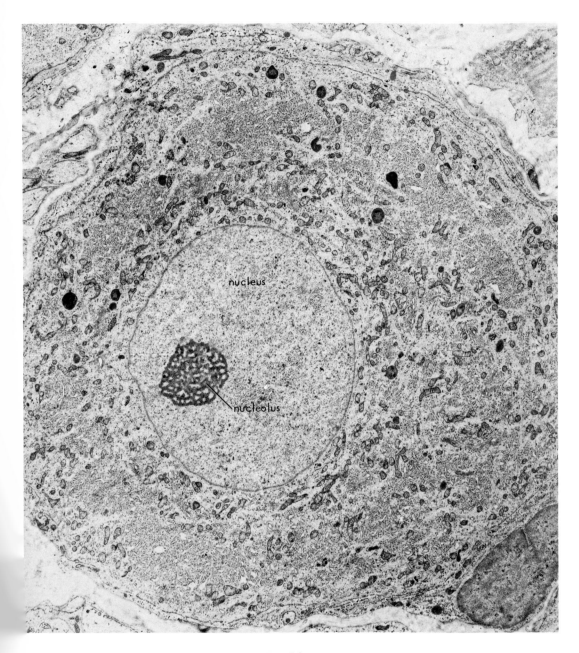

Fig. 86.

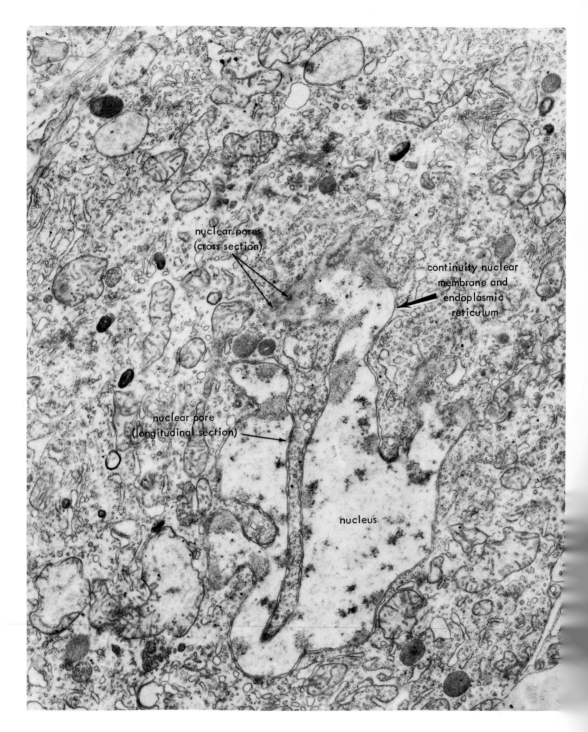

Fig. 87. Double nuclear membrane continuous with endoplasmic reticulum. Nuclear pores are visible in longitudinal and cross section. The nuclear chromatin in nerve cells is sparse, thus producing the clear appearance of this nucleus. Dog cerebellar neuron. $\times$ 20,000.

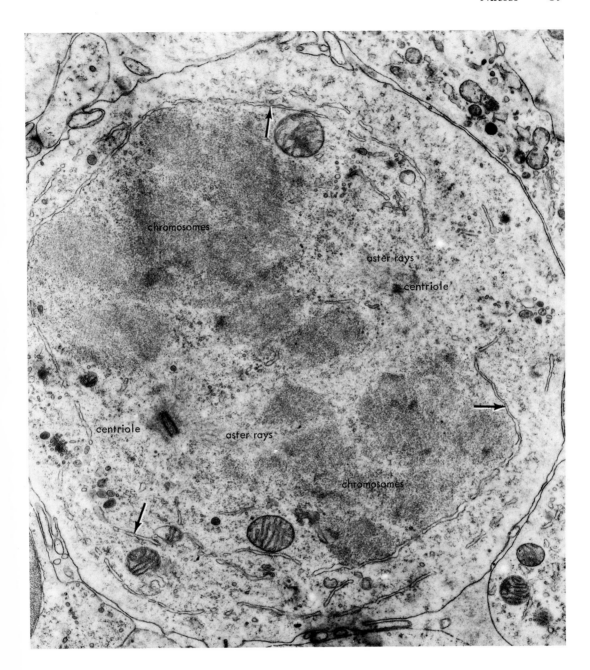

Fig. 88. Lymphoblast in mitosis. Chromosomes are represented by dense material in central portion of cell. The nuclear membrane has broken into smaller membranes (arrows) which are dispersed throughout the cell. Human bone marrow, chronic lymphocytic leukemia. × 16,000.

organism. Only a minute amount of this information can be used by any single cell; the bulk of the information is somehow "blocked," thus differentiating one cell from another. For example, a human liver cell has all the characteristics, physical and biochemical, of the particular human encoded into its nucleus, but it utilizes only that information that makes it function as a liver cell.

The information coded into the deoxyribose nucleic acid must be conveyed from the nucleus to the cytoplasm where the work of a cell takes place. For example, if a pancreatic acinar cell is to form zymogen granules the nucleus must convey to the cytoplasm the information of how to do this task. It is thought that the nucleus manufactures ribose nucleic acid which is then transported to the cytoplasm conveying the information of the nucleus. This form of ribose nucleic acid is called *messenger RNA* (messenger ribose nucleic acid). The messenger RNA attaches along the endoplasmic reticulum and functions as a template for the manufacture of zymogen.

There are many theories concerning the interaction between nucleolar ribose nucleic acid, messenger ribose nucleic acid, and cytoplasmic ribose nucleic acid, but proof of any of these theories is yet to be demonstrated.

REFERENCES

BENNETT, H.: Fine structure of cell nucleus, chromosomes, nucleoli, and membrane, in *Biophysical Science—A Study Program*, edited by J. Oncley, F. Schmitt, R. Williams, M. Rosenberg, and R. Bolt, pp. 297–300. John Wiley & Sons, New York, 1959.

BENZER, S.: The fine structure of the gene. Sci. Amer., **206**:70–84, 1962.

HARRIS, P., and D. MAZIA: The finer structure of the mitotic apparatus, in *The Interpretation of Ultrastructure*, edited by R. Harris, pp. 279–305. Academic Press, Inc., New York, 1962.

MOSES, M.: Breakdown and reformation of the nuclear envelope at cell division, in *IV International Conference on Electron Microscopy, Berlin*, Sept. 10–17, 1958, pp. 230–233. Springer-Verlag, Berlin, 1960.

PORTER, K.: Problems in the study of nuclear fine structure, in *IV International Conference on Electron Microscopy, Berlin*, Sept. 10–17, 1958, pp. 186–198. Springer-Verlag, Berlin, 1960.

RIS, H.: Interpretation of ultrastructure in the cell nucleus, in *The Interpretation of Ultrastructure*, edited by R. Harris, pp. 69–87. Academic Press, Inc., New York, 1962.

SWIFT, H.: The fine structure of annulate lamellae. J. Biophys. Biochem. Cytol., Suppl., **2**:415–418, 1956.

WATSON, M.: Further observations on the nuclear envelope of the animal cell. J. Biophys. Biochem. Cytol., **6**:147–156, 1959.

WISCHNITZER, S.: The ultrastructure of the nucleus and nucleocytoplasmic relations. Intern. Rev. Cytol., **10**:137–162, 1960.

TISSUES

INTRODUCTION

The purpose of cytology is not only to gain an accurate morphological knowledge of the cell and its constituents, but also to learn the relationships and functions of different cells to each other. The condition of cells is closely related to the milieu in which the cells are located. In in vitro tissue culture cellular activity depends a great deal upon the medium. In vivo cellular activity depends a great deal upon its medium, the blood, lymph, and other tissues with which the cells are associated. Part III will describe the fine structure of the basic tissues (epithelial, muscle, nerve, and connective tissues) of the body.

15

EPITHELIAL TISSUE

Epithelium is a cellular tissue that lines a free surface either externally or internally. It is classified in terms of the shape of individual cells: squamous, cuboidal, and columnar; and, the number of layers of cells that comprise the epithelium: simple, pseudostratified, stratified and transitional (Figs. 99, 101, 108, 110, and 117).

Squamous cells are flattened cells that have tapered ends and a thickened central portion where the nucleus is located (Figs. 89, 90, 91, 92, 93, and 119). Cuboidal cells are those whose dimensions essentially are equal in all directions (Figs. 101 to 106). Columnar cells are those whose height exceeds other dimensions (Figs. 95 to 100).

SIMPLE EPITHELIUM

Simple epithelium occurs as a layer one-cell thick with all the cells resting on a basement membrane (see Chap. 18) (Figs. 90, 93, 97, 100, 102, 104, and 119). Pseudostratified epithelium is characterized by all cells resting on the basement membrane, but not all cells extending to the free surface, thus creating the appearance of multiple layers of cells that have different sizes and shapes. Stratified epithelium is composed of "stacks" of cells where one cell rests upon another in layers and only the basal layer of cells rests on a basement membrane (Figs. 108 to 111).

Simple squamous epithelium is found in the rete testis, collecting tubules of the kid-

neys, and tympanic membranes. Endothelium of blood vessels and mesothelium lining the body cavities (pleural, pericardial, and peritoneal cavities) are considered to be simple squamous epithelium although they are developmentally different from other squamous epithelium (Figs. 90, 93, and 119). Simple cuboidal epithelium is found in many ducts, the thyroid, the retina, the lens, and the functional cells of many glands (Figs. 102 to 106). Therefore, cuboidal epithelium is the major secretory tissue of the body. Simple columnar epithelium lines the digestive tract, kidney tubules, and other excretory ducts (Figs. 22, and 95 to 100).

PSEUDOSTRATIFIED EPITHELIUM

Generally only columnar cells are considered to form pseudostratified epithelium. This type of epithelium is characteristic of the respiratory system and male genital system (Fig. 23).

STRATIFIED EPITHELIUM

In many places squamous epithelium is found in the stratified arrangement (stratified squamous epithelium), such as in the skin, the esophagus, the oral cavity, the anus, and the urethra (Figs. 109 and 111). In this type of epithelium the cells resting on the basement membrane are somewhat cuboidal and the more superficial cells are progressively flatter

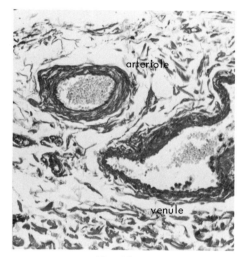

Fig. 89.

Fig. 89. Light micrograph of an arteriole and a venule. Lamina propria of dog esophagus. Allochrome stain. $\times$ 270.

Fig. 90. Simple squamous cells of endothelium of arteriole and venule. Lamina propria of dog esophagus. $\times$ 4,500.

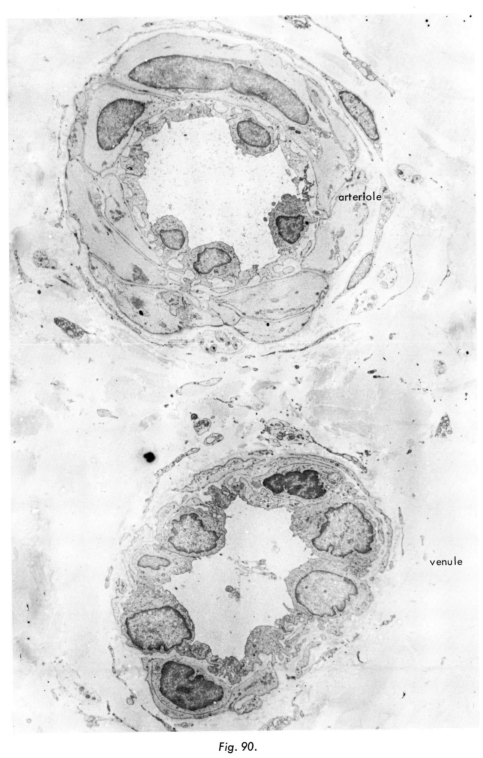

Fig. 90.

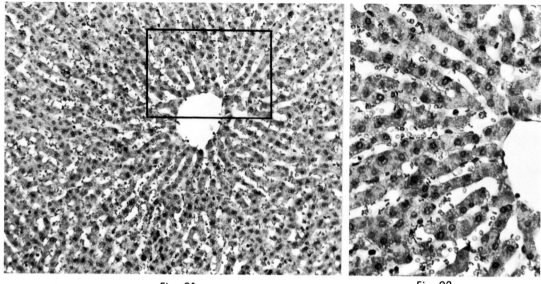

Fig. 91.   Fig. 92.

Fig. 91. Light micrograph of dog liver. Boxed area is shown in Figure 92. Hematoxylin and eosin stain. $\times$ 125.

Fig. 92. Light micrograph of dog liver showing liver sinusoids. Hematoxylin and eosin stain. $\times$ 250.

Fig. 93. Endothelial cell lining liver sinusoids, and separating sinusoid from space of Disse. Note microvilli of liver cells extending into space of Disse. Dog. $\times$ 16,000.

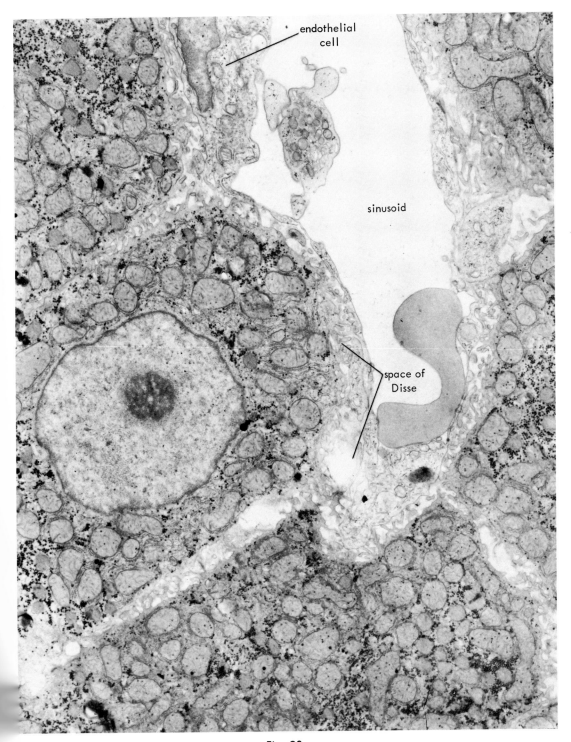

Fig. 93.

toward the free surface. Stratified squamous epithelium also forms the thymic corpuscles (Figs. 112 to 115). Stratified cuboidal epithelium exists in the ovarian follicles, the sebaceous glands, and the ducts of the sweat glands (Figs. 105, 106). Stratified columnar epithelium is rare, existing at the junction of stratified squamous and pseudostratified columnar epithelia, such as in the larynx. The lining of the seminiferous tubules of the testis is either stratified cuboidal or stratified columnar epithelia.

TRANSITIONAL EPITHELIUM

Transitional epithelium is a multilayered type in which the number of layers and cells changes shape in response to external mechanical stimuli (Figs. 116 and 117). This type of epithelium is supposed to represent an intermediate form between columnar or cuboidal and squamous epithelia. Transitional epithelium lines the kidney pelvis, ureters, and urinary bladder (Fig. 118). The shape of the cells in this type of epithelium is a function of the degree of distention of the organ and does not reflect basic changes within the cell. In the contracted urinary bladder, for example, the epithelial cells immediately facing the free surface are cuboidal, the central layers of cells are various shapes, and the basal cells are cuboidal or columnar. With distention of the urinary bladder, the basal cells remain essentially cuboidal, while the cells of the other layers assume a squamous shape.

SURFACE SPECIALIZATION OF EPITHELIAL CELLS

Epithelium may be further subdivided based on specializations of the cell surface or specific products of the cell (Figs. 94, 120, and 123). For example, the pseudostratified columnar epithelium that lines the trachea and bronchi has cilia on the free surface, thus this epithelium is called pseudostratified ciliated columnar epithelium (Fig. 23). Most cuboidal and columnar epithelial cells have microvilli on their free surface, and when these are suf-

ficiently numerous the epithelium is described as having a brush or striated border (Figs. 18, 19, 22, 100, 102, and 119). The superficial squamous cells of skin develop keratin granules and become keratinized (cornified, "horny"), and are then referred to as keratinized or cornified squamous epithelium (Fig. 111). Columnar cells (goblet cells) may form mucous and numerous other secretions, depending on the particular cell (Figs. 59, and 121 to 123). The luminal surface of transitional cells is usually scalloped.

INTERNAL STRUCTURE OF EPITHELIAL CELLS

The internal structure of epithelial cells varies with function and cell type. There is a tendency, however, to follow a basic pattern with each cell type (squamous, cuboidal, or columnar). Generally, a single nucleus is present, which in squamous cells may be ovoid; in cuboidal cells, spherical; and in columnar cells, elongate or cylindrical. Rarely, there may be a double nucleus, as in liver cells. The longitudinal axis of the nucleus usually parallels the longitudinal axis of the cell. Mitochondria are arranged around the nucleus in squamous cells. In columnar cells the mitochondria, usually elongate, are arranged parallel to the long axis of the cell, mainly above and below the nucleus. Fine fibrils (cell web) are common in epithelial cells. They are especially prominent in stratified squamous epithelial cells. The cell axis in columnar epithelium is perpendicular to the lumen lined by the cells, while in squamous epithelium the axis of the cell generally parallels the free surface. Fusiform vesicles are found within the transitional cell cytoplasm, and are prominent near the luminal surface. It has been postulated that these vesicles represent infolded plasma membrane which is pinched off during change of cell shape, or reservoirs of fluid (water) removed from the cells.

Junctional complexes (consisting of the zonula occludens, zonula adhaerens, and desmosome or macula adhaerens) bind the epithelial cells together (Figs. 18, 20, 109, and 114).

Variations in the basic structure of the junctional complex may occur in various epithelia. The line of fusion (*zonula occludens*) is more prominent in the epithelia of the stomach and colon than in epithelia of other areas. The zonula occludens may be poorly developed in epithelia of the thyroid, liver, pancreas, and some salivary glands (Figs. 18, 102, and 104). The *zonula adhaerens* may not be prominent in the epithelia of the uterus and oviduct. The desmosome may be poorly developed or absent from the simple squamous epithelium of capillaries (endothelium) and the peritoneum (mesothelium).

REFERENCES

ALBRIGHT, J.: Electron microscope studies of keratinization as observed in gingiva and cheek mucosa. Ann. New York Acad. Sci., 85:351–361, 1960.

EKHOLM, R. and F. SJÖSTRAND: The ultrastructural organization of the mouse thyroid gland. J. Ultrast. Res., 1:178–199, 1957.

FARQUHAR, M. and G. PALADE: Junctional complexes in various epithelia. J. Cell Biol., 17:375–412, 1963.

FAWCETT, D. and K. PORTER: A study of the fine structure of ciliated epithelia. J. Morph., 94:221–282, 1954.

FAWCETT, D.: Observations on the cytology and electron microscopy of the hepatic cells. J. Nat. Cancer Inst., Suppl., 15:1475–1502, 1955.

HELANDER, H.: Ultrastructure of fundus glands in the mouse gastric mucosa. J. Ultrast. Res., Suppl. 4, 1964.

KOHNEN, P., and L. WEISS: An electron microscopic study of thymic corpuscles. Anat. Rec., 148:29–57, 1964.

NORRIS, J.: The normal histology of the esophageal and gastric mucosae of the frog, *Rana pipiens*. J. Exper. Zool., 141:155–173, 1959.

ODOR, D.: Observations of the rat mesothelium with the electron and phase microscopes. Amer. J. Anat., 95:433–466, 1954.

RHODIN, J.: Electron microscopy of the kidney, in *Renal Disease*, edited by D. Black, pp. 117–156. Blackwell Scientific Publications, Oxford, 1962.

WALKER, B.: Electron microscopic observations on transitional epithelium of the mouse urinary bladder. J. Ultrast. Res., 3:345–361, 1961.

YAMADA, E.: The fine structure of the gall bladder epithelium of the mouse. J. Biophys. Biochem. Cytol., 1:445–458, 1955.

ZETTERQUIST, H.: The ultrastructural organization of the columnar cells of the mouse jejunum. Thesis, Karolinska Institute, Aktiebolaget Godvil, Stockholm, 1956.

Fig. 94. Three-dimensional schematic representation of epithelial cells (*podocytes*) of visceral layer of Bowman's capsule of kidney glomerulus. (Redrawn and modified from: Ultrastructure of the Renal Glomerulus, Eaton Laboratories, Norwich, New York.)

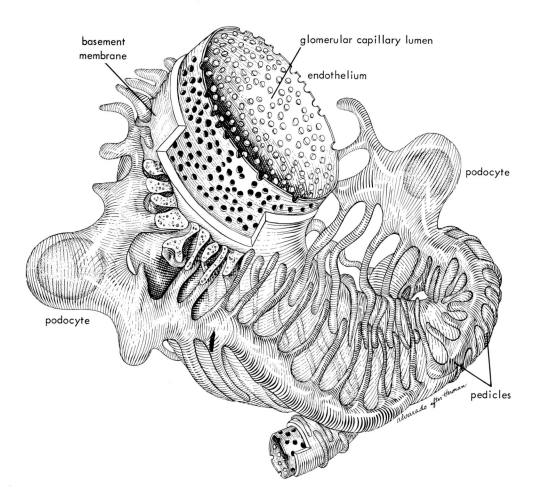

Fig. 94.

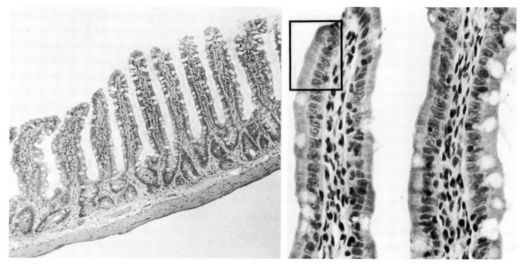

Fig. 95.   Fig. 96.

Fig. 95. Light micrograph of rat jejunum. Hematoxylin and eosin stain. $\times$ 120.

Fig. 96. Light micrograph of simple columnar epithelium. Rat jejunum. Boxed area is comparable to electron micrograph of Figure 97. Hematoxylin and eosin stain. $\times$ 600.

Fig. 97. Panoramic view of simple columnar epithelium with underlying basement membrane and lamina propria. Rat ileum. $\times$ 4,900.

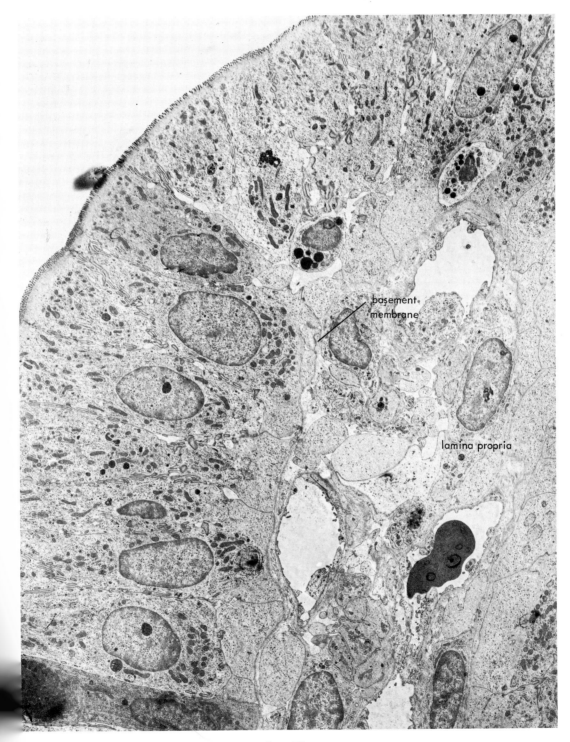

basement
membrane

lamina propria

Fig. 97.

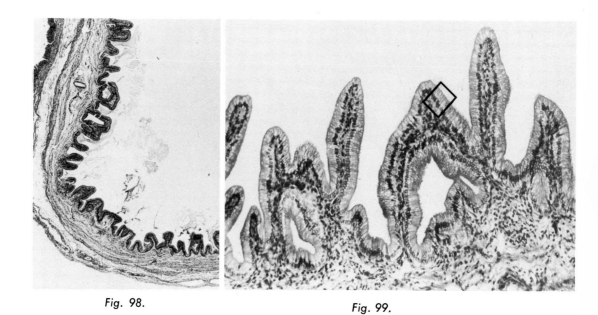

Fig. 98.   *Fig. 99.*

Fig. 98. Light micrograph of the wall of the gall bladder. Dog. Hematoxylin and eosin stain. $\times$ 30.

Fig. 99. Light micrograph of simple columnar epithelium of dog gall bladder. Boxed area is comparable to electron micrograph of Figure 100. Hematoxylin and eosin stain. $\times$ 150.

Fig. 100. Simple columnar epithelial cells. Dog gall bladder. $\times$ 6,500.

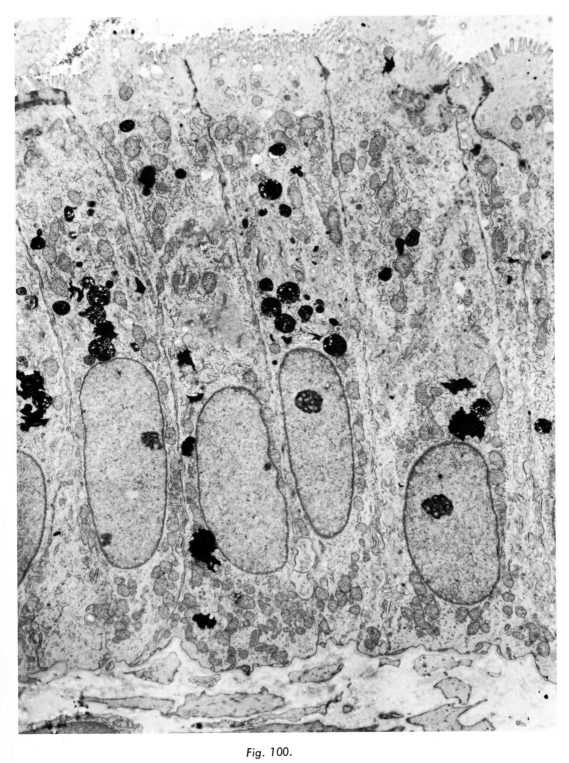

Fig. 100.

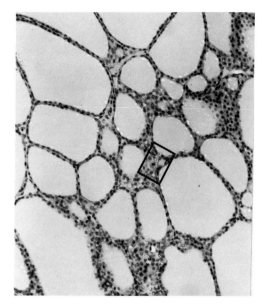

Fig. 101.

Fig. 101. Light micrograph of dog thyroid. Boxed area is comparable **to electron** micrograph of Figure 102. Hematoxylin and eosin stain. $\times$ 130.

Fig. 102. Simple **cuboidal** cells. Dog thyroid. $\times$ 5,600.

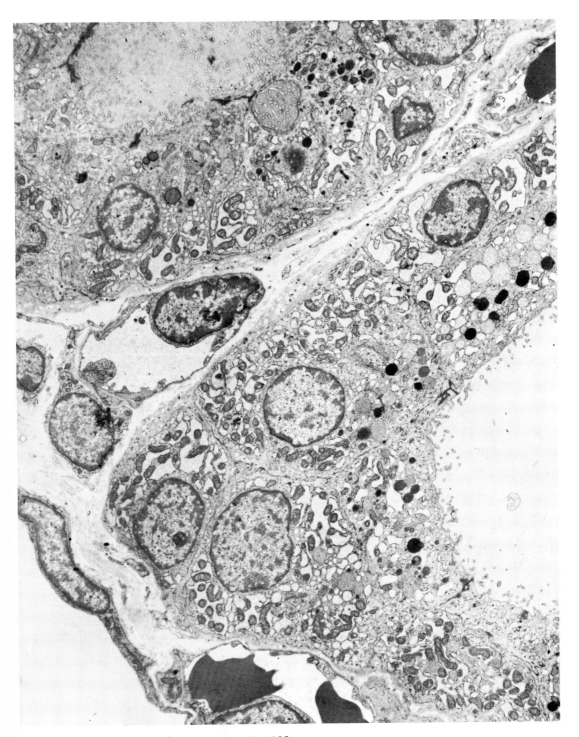

Fig. 102.

Fig. 103. Panoramic view of secretory cuboidal cells. Guinea pig submaxillary gland. $\times$ 4,400.

Fig. 104. Pyramidal shaped secretory cuboidal epithelial cell. Guinea pig submaxillary gland. $\times$ 14,000.

Fig. 103.

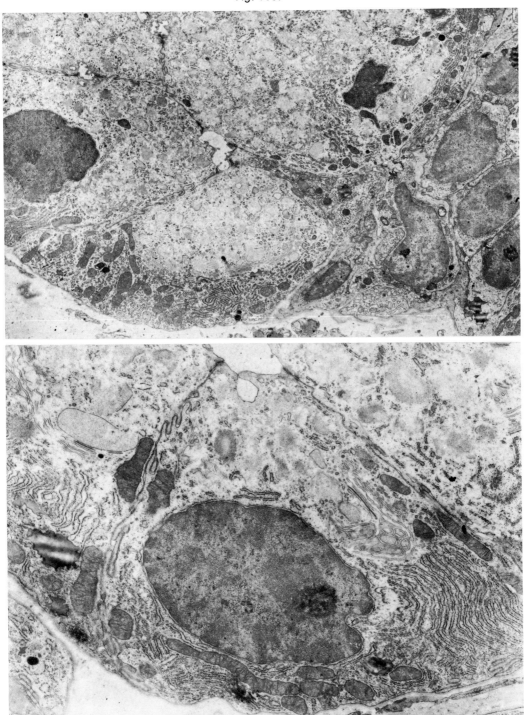

Fig. 104.

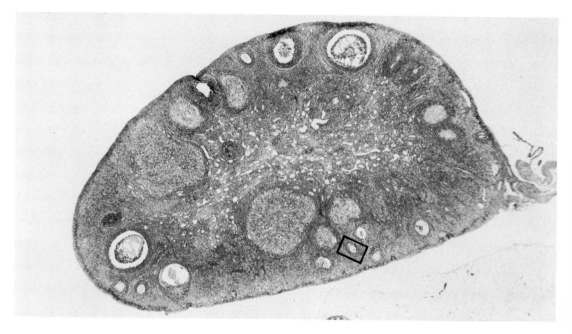

Fig. 105.

Fig. 105. Light micrograph of a dog ovary. Boxed follicle is comparable to electron micrograph of Figure 106. Hematoxylin and eosin stain. × 20.

Fig. 106. Simple cuboidal cells surrounding ovarian germinal cell. Microvilli of cuboidal cells face a potential lumen, and as germinal cell matures lumen becomes visible. Dog. × 5,400.

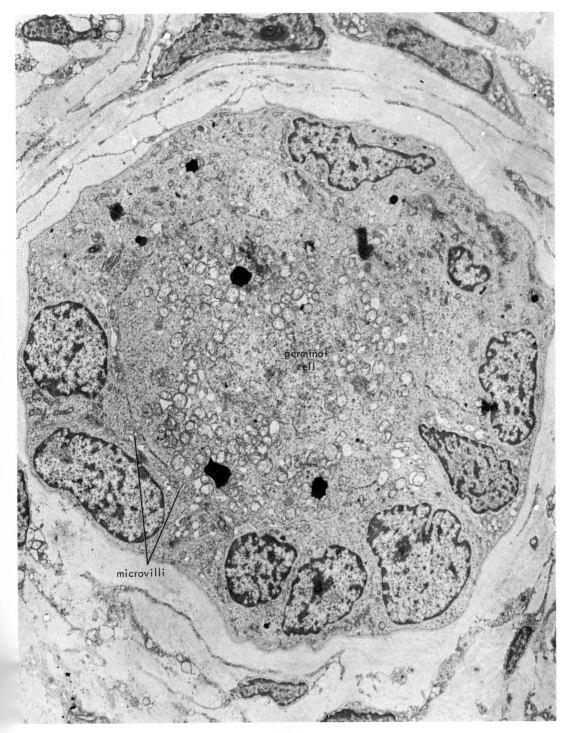

Fig. 106.

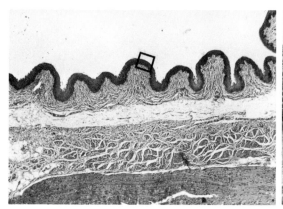

Fig. 107.

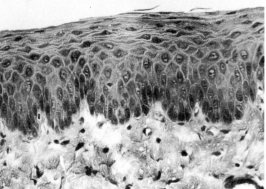

Fig. 108.

Fig. 107. Light micrograph of dog esophagus. Boxed area is comparable to Figure 108. Hematoxylin and eosin stain. ✕ 30.

Fig. 108. Light micrograph of stratified squamous epithelium. Dog esophagus. Hematoxylin and eosin stain. ✕ 540.

Fig. 109. Stratified squamous epithelium. Dog esophagus. ✕ 4,100.

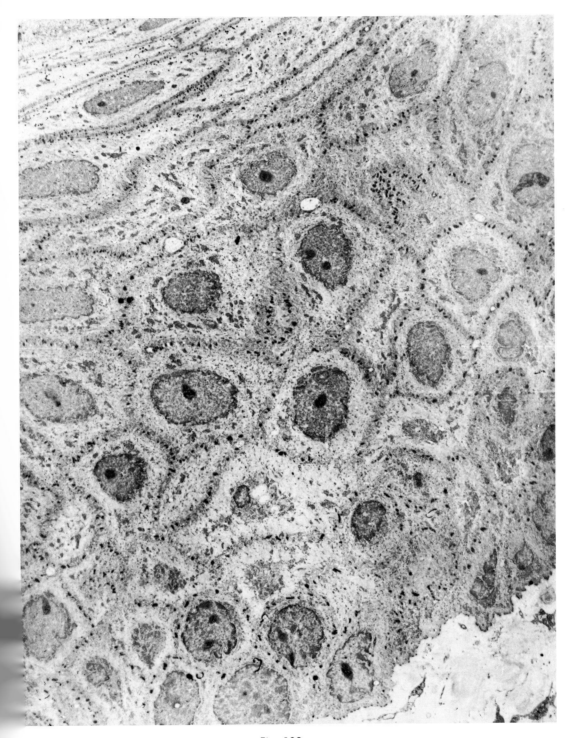

Fig. 109.

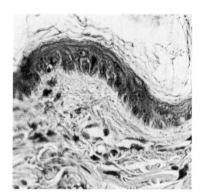

Fig. 110.

Fig. 110. Light micrograph of dog skin. Compare with electron micrograph of Figure 111. Hematoxylin and eosin stain. × 300.

Fig. 111. Cornified epithelium. Note keratohyaline granules in superficial squamous cells. Dog skin. × 8,100.

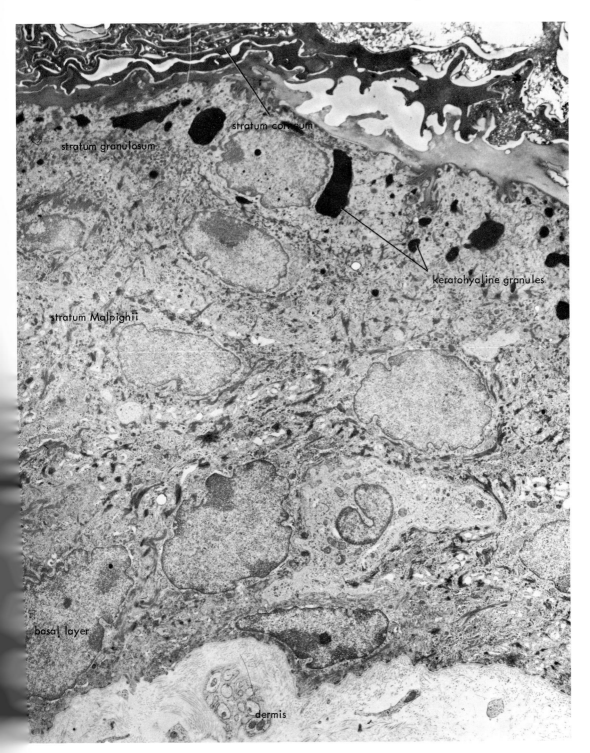

Fig. 111.

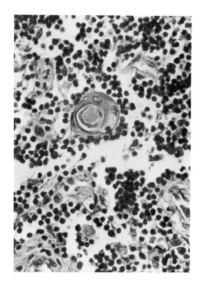

Fig. 112.

Fig. 112. Light micrograph of human thymic corpuscle. Hematoxylin and eosin stain. × 300.

Fig. 113. Hassall's bodies (*thymic corpuscles*) are concentrically arranged squamous epithelial cells that contain keratohyaline granules. Cystic degeneration of the center of the corpuscle frequently occurs and masses of keratin and cellular debris become prominent. Human. × 6,300.

Fig. 114. Squamous cells of thymic corpuscles are held together by junctional complexes. Human. × 4,500.

Fig. 115. Fine fibrils, similar to tonofibrils, are found in the thymic corpuscle. These cells occasionally contain a fibrous element reminiscent of muscle myofilaments. Human. × 20,000.

Fig. 113.

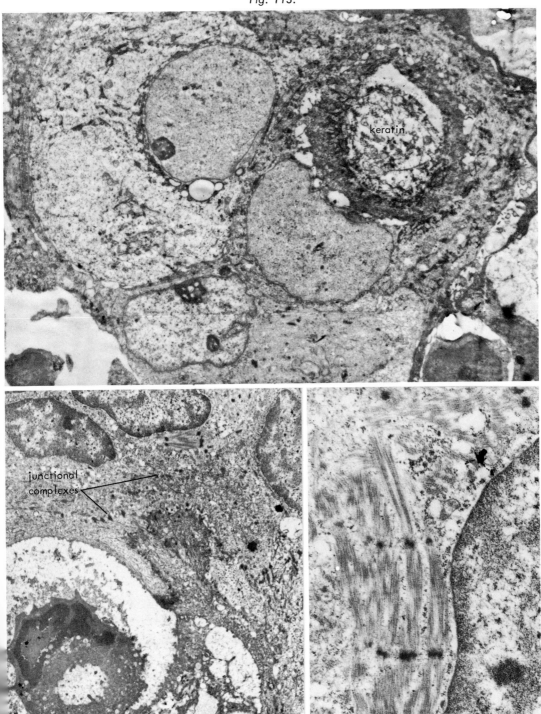

Fig. 114.

Fig. 115.

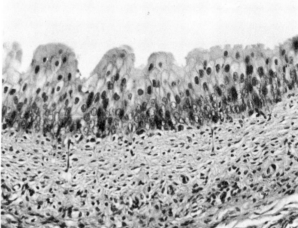

Fig. 116.   Fig. 117.

Fig. 116. Light micrograph of dog ureter. Boxed area is shown in Figure 117. Hematoxylin and eosin stain. $\times$ 45.

Fig. 117. Light micrograph of transitional epithelium of dog ureter. Compare with electron micrograph of Figure 118. Hematoxylin and eosin stain. $\times$ 330.

Fig. 118. Transitional epithelial cells. Dog ureter. $\times$ 9,000.

Fig. 119. Simple squamous cell of peritoneum (mesothelium). Dog. $\times$ 8,300.

Fig. 118.

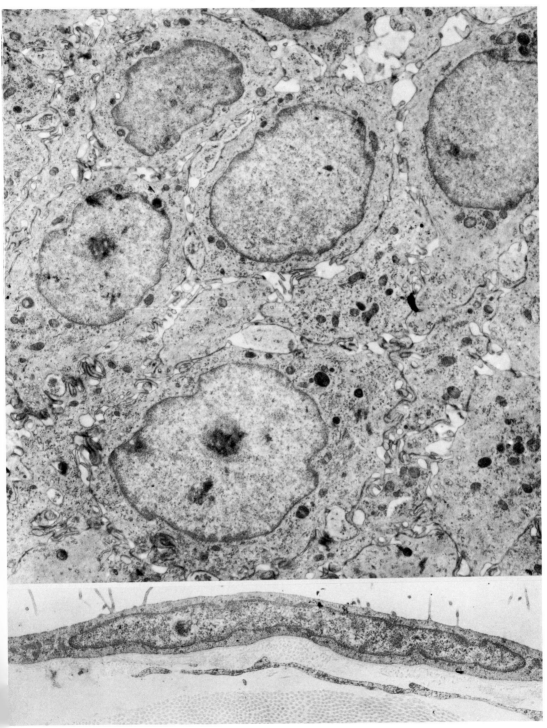

Fig. 119.

Fig. 120. Cytoplasm of epithelial podocyte is drawn into long processes with smaller interdigitating "feet" (*pedicles*) which attach to basement membrane. Spaces between pedicles are called *slit pores*. Rat kidney glomerulus. $\times$ 8,000.

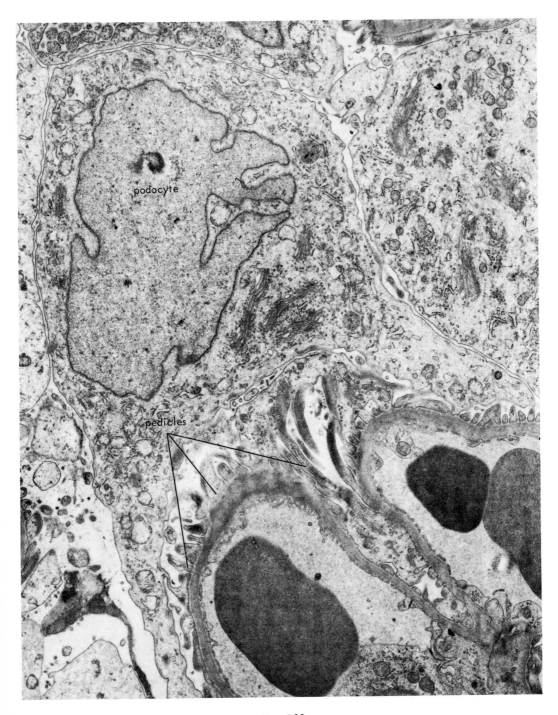

Fig. 120.

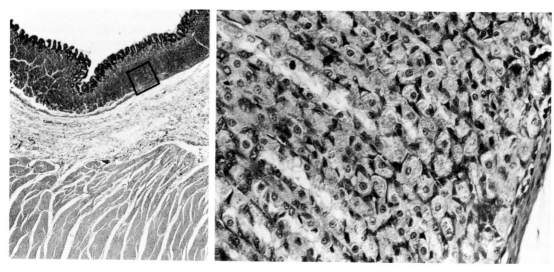

Fig. 121.   Fig. 122.

Fig. 121. Light micrograph of rat stomach. Boxed area is shown in Figure 122. Hematoxylin and eosin stain. × 20.

Fig. 122. Light micrograph of cells of gastric glands. Rat stomach. Hematoxylin and eosin stain. × 270.

Fig. 123. Epithelial cells distinguished by specific products of cells. Rat stomach. × 8,100.

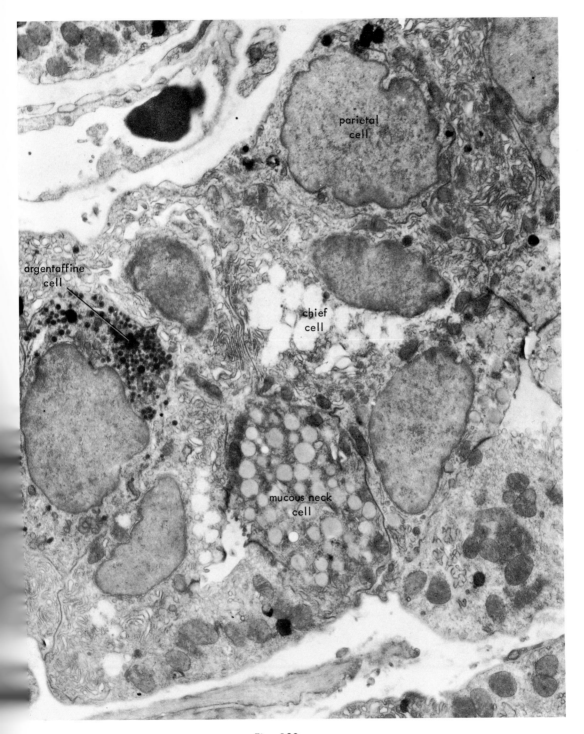

Fig. 123.

16

MUSCLE TISSUE

Muscle is a tissue that converts chemical energy to kinetic energy. There are two forms of muscle in vertebrates, striated and smooth. In general, striated muscle is subject to voluntary control, except for cardiac muscle, which is involuntary. Smooth muscle is involuntary, except for the smooth muscle of the urinary bladder which is under voluntary control. Muscle cells are oriented with their long axes in the direction of contraction, and they usually are grouped into bundles (Figs. 124 and 128). The contraction of muscle provides for varied functions such as locomotion, peristalsis, vascular tone, pumping blood, constricting bronchioles, and constricting the pupil of the eye.

STRIATED MUSCLE

Striated muscle, skeletal muscle and cardiac muscle, is composed of closely packed groups of elongated cylindrical cells (fibers) (Figs. 124 and 125). With the light microscope, individual muscle fibers appear enveloped by a sheath of reticular fibers. Corresponding to the reticular fibers seen with the light microscope, in electron microscopy the muscle cells are seen to be surrounded by a basement membrane about 500 Ångstroms thick in which are embedded unit fibers of collagen (see Chap. 8).

The dimensions of fibers vary between and within species, muscle types, and muscle groups depending on the work required of the cell. Each fiber is surrounded by a plasma membrane (*sarcolemma*). Numerous pinocytotic vesicles occur as invaginations of the plasma membrane, and measure about 300 to 400 Ångstroms across (Fig. 132). The cytoplasm of muscle fibers is called *sarcoplasm*.

The distinctive feature of striated muscle fibers is the presence of sarcoplasmic myofibrils with cross-striations (Figs. 125 and 127). The striations, which are perpendicular to the long axis of the myofibril, are aligned in register from fibril to fibril, producing the uniform cross-striated appearance seen with the light microscope (Fig. 124). Two major bands of striation are readily visualized with the light microscope; the A band (*anisotropic*) rotates a beam of polarized light, and the I band (*isotropic*) does not rotate polarized light. Figure 126 is a schematic drawing of a portion of a myofibril illustrating its fine structure. In the middle of the I band there is a dark zone called the Z band. The unit of structure between Z bands is known as the *sarcomere*. The dense Z band consists of an amorphous substance that has yet to be further characterized. In the middle of the A band there is a less dense area called the H band, and in the center of the H band is a thin zone of increased density referred to as the M band. The fibril is composed of still smaller units, *myofilaments*. Two forms of myofilaments have been found, one thick (100 Ångstroms in diameter), and the other thin (50 Ångstroms in diameter). Thick filaments are found

125

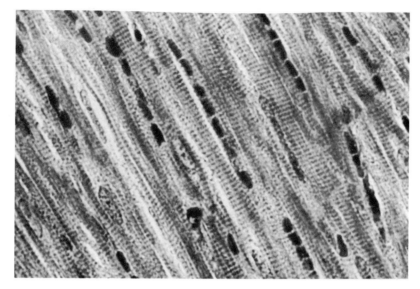

Fig. 124.

Fig. 124. Light micrograph of a longitudinal section of rat cardiac muscle showing cross striations. Compare with electron micrograph of Figure 125. Iron hematoxylin stain. $\times$ 800.

Fig. 125. Low magnification electron micrograph of rat cardiac muscle showing banding and numerous sarcosomes. A capillary containing an erythrocyte is present (*upper left*). $\times$ 8,100.

Fig. 125.

exclusively in the A band and course the entire width of this band. The density of the M band appears to be due to a focal thickening of the thick filaments at this point. The fine filaments course through the I band, extending variable distances into the A band. In a cross section of an A band it can be seen that each thick filament is surrounded by six fine filaments in hexagonal array (Fig. 133). These are minute spines along the length of the thick filaments at intervals of 60 to 70 Ångstroms that extend toward the neighboring fine filaments (Fig. 133).

Studies of the chemical composition of myofilaments indicate that the contractile protein *actin* is located in the thin filament, and *myosin* is located in the thick filament. It has long been known that the I band shortens during muscular contraction; the A band shortens only slightly (in the later stages of contraction); and the H band diminishes in breadth. It has been hypothesized that during contraction the length of the filaments does not change appreciably, but there occurs a sliding of the thin filaments into the A band, thus shortening the I and H bands.

Between the myofibrils in the sarcoplasm there is an extensive system of smooth-surfaced endoplasmic reticulum (Figs. 45, 131, and 134). This reticulum has an orderly arrangement in concert with the striations of the fibrils. At the extremity of each A band, near the I band, there are two large profiles of smooth-surfaced endoplasmic reticulum separated by a smaller profile, running perpendicular to the direction of the filament. Between these larger profiles of endoplasmic reticulum there are numerous smaller elongate profiles running parallel to the myofibril and connecting with the larger profiles. In three dimensions there is thus an extensive and ordered arrangement of endoplasmic reticulum encasing each myofibril (Fig. 131). It has been postulated that the endoplasmic reticulum connects with pinocytotic vesicles of the plasma membrane within the fiber. The endoplasmic reticulum probably functions in nerve impulse transmission. The pinocytotic vesicles may function in transport of material across the plasma membrane, and possibly may somehow function in nerve transmission.

In addition to the endoplasmic reticulum there are many mitochondria and varying amounts of lipid and glycogen located between the fibrils. Mitochondria in muscle are called *sarcosomes* (Fig. 127). Lipofuscin pigment can be seen in aging muscle (Fig. 135). Nuclei are located peripherally in skeletal muscle fibers and centrally in cardiac muscle fibers (Figs. 124 and 128).

Cardiac muscle differs in several respects from skeletal muscle, aside from the type of nervous control. Cardiac muscle has more numerous sarcosomes than skeletal muscle. Intercalated discs, present only in cardiac muscle, are areas of marked interdigitation of apposing plasma membranes giving a "hand-in-glove" appearance (Figs. 130 and 132). There is an intermittent accumulation of dense material (S zones) in the sarcoplasm along the intercalated discs which represents the desmosomes of cardiac muscle (Fig. 132). There are no bridges of sarcoplasm extending from one fiber to another; the fibers are clearly separate and not a syncytium. The fine structure of the myofibrils is the same in cardiac and skeletal muscle.

SMOOTH MUSCLE

Smooth muscle cells (fibers) have the same basic morphology throughout the body, al-

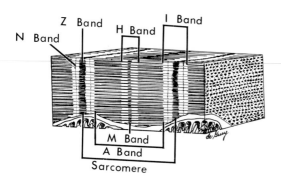

Fig. 126. Three-dimensional schematic representation of the banding of muscle.

though smooth muscle is found in a wide variety of tissues. The fibers are fusiform in shape and measure about 0.2 millimeters long and 6 microns wide, although in the pregnant uterus the fibers may reach a length greater than 0.5 millimeters. The elongate nucleus is located in the center of the cytoplasm at the broadest portion of the fiber and during contraction the nucleus may appear folded or twisted (Fig. 136). Reticular fibers encase each smooth muscle fiber (see Chap. 18). Pinocytotic vesicles are numerous along the plasma membrane, and these vesicles are similar in morphology to those described in striated muscle (Fig. 137). The bulk of the cytoplasm is occupied by fine filaments (*myofilaments*) coursing parallel to the long axis of the fiber. With osmium tetroxide fixation, the myofilaments are not visualized, and the cytoplasm appears nearly homogeneous (Fig. 137). Fusiform densities, which occur within the cytoplasm and along the plasma membrane, are local aggregates of myofilaments (Fig. 137). The smooth muscle fiber contains all the usual cell organelles, but these are few in number, and are located at each pole of the nucleus (Figs. 136 and 137).

Unlike skeletal muscle, where each fiber functions independently, smooth muscle transmits nerve impulses from fiber to fiber resulting in rhythmic contraction. Fibers that transmit nerve impulses rapidly, such as those in the esophagus, are more closely packed than fibers that transmit impulses slowly, such as those in the colon. No cytoplasmic continuity exists between smooth muscle fibers, although close contact of the plasma membranes frequently is found in smooth muscle fibers where intercellular transmission of impulse is rapid.

REFERENCES

BENNETT, H.: The structure of striated muscle as seen by the electron microscope, in *Structure and Function of Muscle*, Vol. I, edited by J. Bourne, pp. 137–182. Academic Press, Inc., New York, 1960.

BOZLER, E.: Smooth Muscle, in *Muscle as a Tissue*, edited by K. Rodahl and S. Horvath, pp. 20–33. McGraw-Hill Book Company, New York, 1962.'

FINEAN, J.: *Chemical Ultrastructure in Living Tissues*, pp. 92–101, Charles C Thomas, Springfield, 1961.

GILEV, V.: A study of myofibril sarcomere structure during contraction. J. Cell Biol., **12**:135–147, 1962.

HARMAN, J., M. O'HEGARTY, and C. BYRNES: The ultrastructure of human smooth muscle. Exper. Mol. Path., 1:204–228, 1962.

HUXLEY, H., and J. HANSON: The molecular basis of contraction in cross-striated muscles, in *Structure and Function of Muscle*, Vol. I, edited by J. Bourne, pp. 183–228. Academic Press, Inc., New York, 1960.

MUSCATELLO, U., E. ANDERSSON-CEDERGREN, G. AZZONE, and A. VON DER DECKEN: The sarcotubular system of frog skeletal muscle. A morphological and biochemical study. J. Biophys. Biochem. Cytol., Suppl., 10:201–218, 1961.

PEACHY, L., and K. PORTER: Intracellular impulse conduction to muscle cells. Science, **129**: 721–722, 1959.

PEASE, D., and W. PAULE: Electron microscopy of elastic arteries; the thoracic aorta of the rat. J. Ultrast. Res., 3:469–483, 1960.

PORTER, K.: The sarcoplasmic reticulum. Its recent history and present status. J. Biophys. Biochem. Cytol., Suppl., 10:219–226, 1961.

PROSSER, C., G. BURNSTOCK, and J. KAHN: Conduction in smooth muscle: comparable structural properties. Amer. J. Physiol., 199:545–552, 1960.

REVEL, J.: The sarcoplasmic reticulum of the bat cricothyroid muscle. J. Cell Biol., **12**:571–588, 1962.

SJÖSTRAND, F., and E. ANDERSSON-CEDERGREN: Intercalated discs of heart muscle, in *Structure and Function of Muscle*, Vol. I, edited by J. Bourne, pp. 421–445. Academic Press, Inc., New York, 1960.

SZENT-GYÖRGYI, A.: Proteins of the myofibril, in *Structure and Function of Muscle*, Vol. II, edited by G. Bourne, pp. 1–54. Academic Press, Inc., New York, 1960.

THAEMERT, J.: Intercellular bridges as protoplasmic anastomoses between smooth muscle cells. J. Biophys. Biochem. Cytol., **6**:67–70, 1959.

Fig. 127. Banding of each fibril is in register with similar banding of adjacent fibrils. Mitochondria, lipid, and glycogen are located between fibrils. Rat cardiac muscle. $\times$ 32,000.

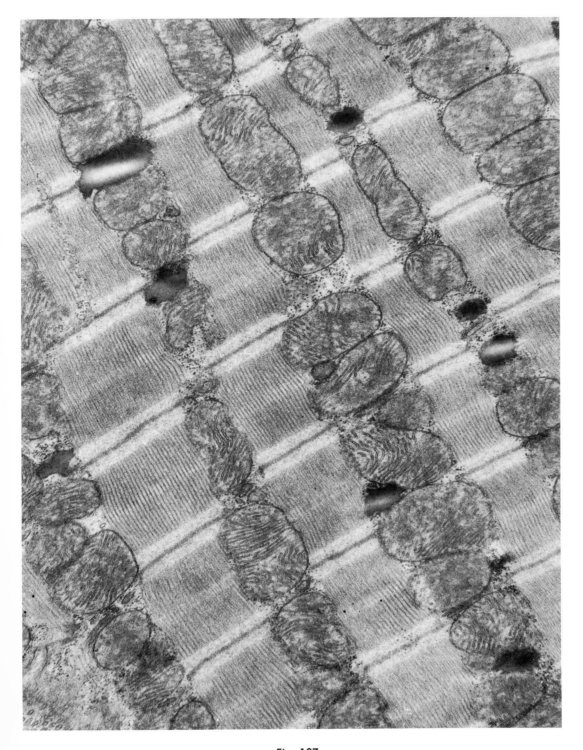

Fig. 127.

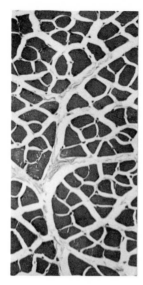

Fig. 128. Light micrograph of a cross section of rat skeletal muscle. Compare with electron micrograph of Figure 129. Hematoxylin and eosin stain. × 165.

Fig. 128.

Fig. 129. Cross section of rat skeletal muscle at A bands with small portion of longitudinal section of adjacent fiber (*upper right*). × 4,700.

Fig. 130. Intercalated disc crossing fibrils at Z band. Rat cardiac muscle. × 14,000.

Fig. 129.

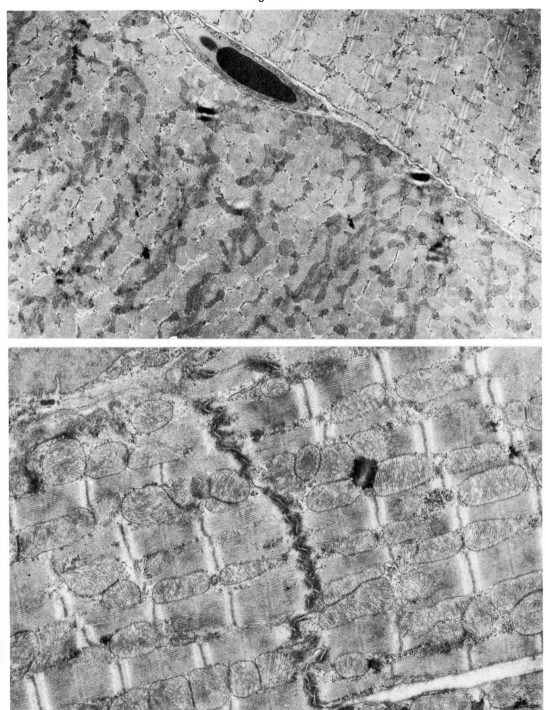

Fig. 130.

Fig. 131. Three-dimensional schematic representation of muscle. Each fibril is enclosed in smooth-surfaced endoplasmic reticulum, note particularly the top two fibrils. The appearance and extent of the reticulum varies between species. The banding is created by thick and thin myofilaments. (Redrawn and modified from concepts of K. Porter and G. Palade, J. Biophys. Biochem. Cytol. **3**:283, 1957).

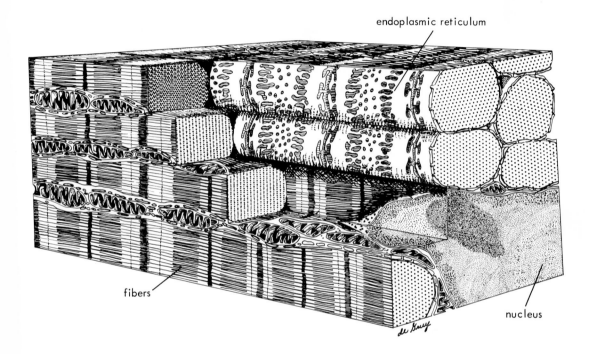

Fig. 132. High magnification of intercalated disc crossing Z band. S zones are evident. Note pinocytotic vesicles of plasma membrane. Rat cardiac muscle. $\times$ 47,000.

Fig. 133. High magnification of cross section of fibril showing cut ends of thick and thin myofilaments. Rat skeletal muscle. $\times$ 79,000.

Fig. 134. Endoplasmic reticulum. Rat cardiac muscle. $\times$ 34,000.

Fig. 135. Aging pigment *(lipofuscin)* adjacent to nucleus. Rat cardiac muscle fibril. $\times$ 13,000.

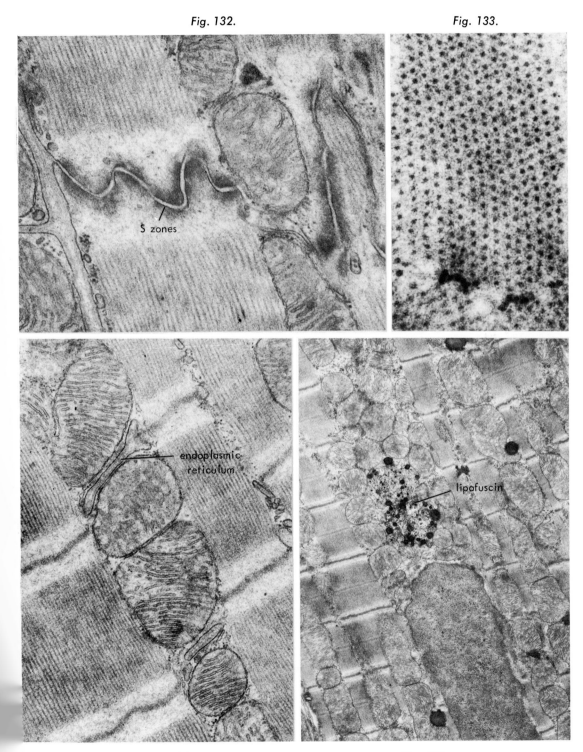

Fig. 132.

Ş zones

Fig. 133.

endoplasmic
reticulum

lipofuscin

Fig. 134.

Fig. 135.

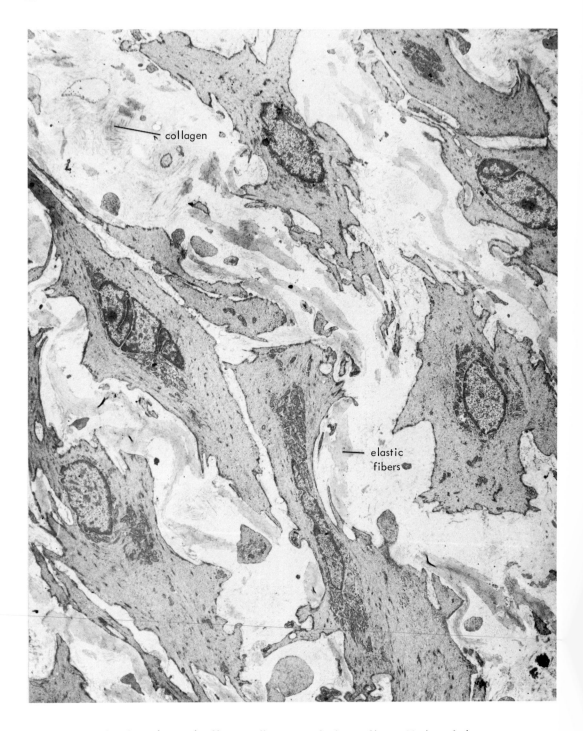

Fig. 136. Smooth muscle fibers, collagen, and elastic fibers. Media of dog aorta.
$\times$ 4,200.

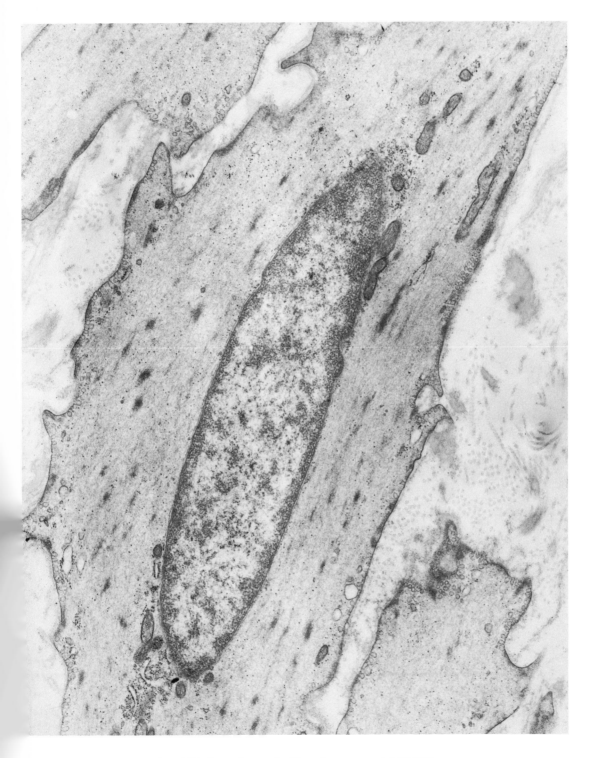

Fig. 137. Smooth muscle fiber. Dog aorta. ✕ 20,000.

17

NERVE TISSUE

The chief characteristic of nerve tissue is that its specialized cells are highly irritable, serving to conduct electrochemical impulses. Nerve tissue also records, by some as yet unknown mechanism, impulses which later can be recalled, the process of learning. The functional unit of this tissue is the nerve cell (*neuron*). Specialized supporting tissue (*neuroglia, neurolemmal cells,* etc.), as well as blood vessels and connective tissue are associated with neurons in the organization of the nervous system.

NEURONS

Neurons, composed of cell bodies (*perikarya*) and their processes (fibers), exist in several different locations such as the cerebral and cerebellar cortices and the spinal ganglia (Figs. 138 to 143). Neurons usually have a large nucleus with sparse chromatin, clean nucleoplasm, and large nucleoli (Figs. 139 and 141). The distinguishing feature of neurons is the basophilic granules (*Nissl, chromophil,* or *tigroid substance*), which in the electron microscope are seen to be loci of flattened sacs of ergastoplasm in parallel array with tubular interconnections (Fig. 139). Numerous ribosomes, not associated with the endoplasmic reticulum, are scattered randomly throughout the cytoplasm (Fig. 46). Nissl substance is absent from the conical origin of the axon (*axon hillock*). The amount of Nissl substance varies from neuron to neuron,

and in certain conditions the rate of protein usage by the neuron may exceed the rate of protein synthesis with subsequent reduction in the amount of Nissl substance, a condition known as *chromatolysis.*

The Golgi complex is extensive and distributed throughout the cytoplasm of neurons (Figs. 140 and 141). In nerve cell injury, such as in poliomyelitis, the Golgi complex may disintegrate and disappear. Melanin granules, the function of which is unknown, can be found in neurons and lipofuscin (aging pigment) and ferritin granules become prominent in some neurons as the animal grows older. A typical centrosome is found in immature cells during embryonic development, but rarely is seen in neurons of adult vertebrates. Moderate numbers of lysosomes are found in neurons. Fine filaments, about 50 Ångstroms in diameter, are randomly distributed in the cytoplasm when studied with the electron microscope. The neurofilaments seen with the light microscope apparently are aggregates of these filaments. Small elongate mitochondria are scattered throughout the perikarya, and are found in large numbers in the axon.

Unlike other neurons, the cerebellar Purkinje cell has no axon hillock. Multivesicular bodies of unknown significance frequently are found in close approximation to the Golgi material in these cells. Subsurface membrane bound systems, theorized to be involved in the transport of material into and out of the neuron, are prominent in Purkinje cells.

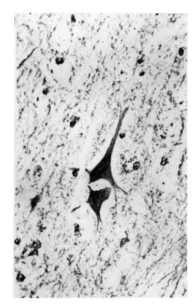

Fig. 138. Light micrograph of motor neurons (*pyramidal cells*) of dog cerebral cortex. Compare with electron micrograph of Figure 139. Bodian's stain. × 300.

Fig. 138.

Fig. 139. Motor neuron. Dog cerebral cortex. × 5,400.

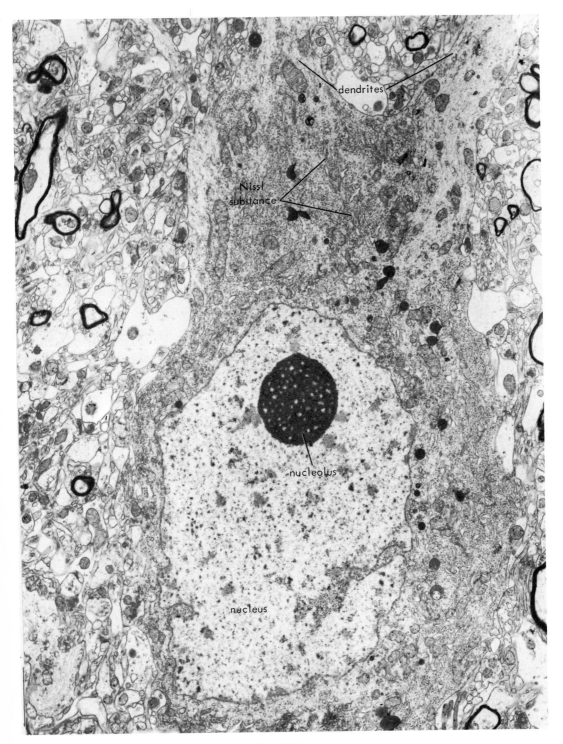

Fig. 139.

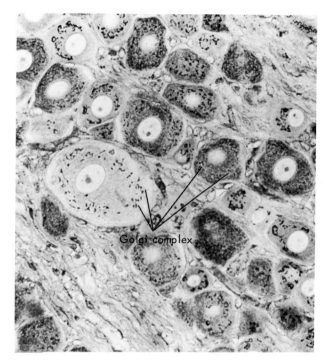

Fig. 140.

Fig. 140. Light micrograph of dorsal root ganglion cells of rabbit. The silver stain demonstrates the extensive Golgi complex. Compare with electron micrograph of Figure 141. Cajal's silver-osmium stain. $\times$ 600.

Fig. 141. Sympathetic ganglion cell with extensive Nissl substance and Golgi complex. Dog. $\times$ 6,300.

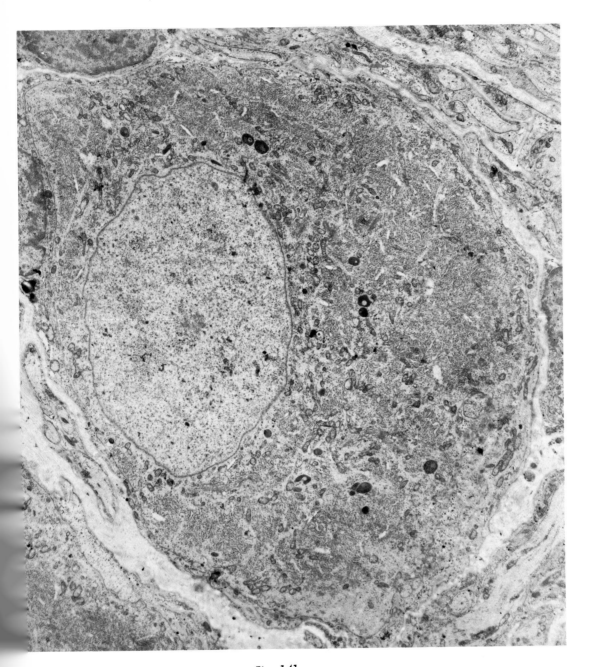

Fig. 141.

Dendrites are direct extensions of the cell body, containing the usual organelles found in the cell (Fig. 139). Axons do not contain Nissl substance, otherwise they have the same fine structure as dendrites (Fig. 143). Progressive decrease in the quantity of Nissl substance occurs in axons a certain distance from the perikarya, making distinction between axons and dendrites difficult. Intermingled with the filaments are slender tubules (200 to 300 Ångstroms in thickness and of unknown length) oriented parallel to the long axis of the fiber. The fine filaments are most numerous in the region of the axon hillock. Several investigators have suggested a 200 Ångstrom pseudo-axial periodicity, giving a beaded appearance to the filaments. Dendrites have many branches and spines connecting with other cells (*synapses*) along their entire course, whereas axons usually have only one connection at the terminal end of the fiber.

Most axons are enclosed by a sheath of refractile material that is responsible for the white color of fresh nerve tissue. This sheath (*myelin sheath; myelin lamellae*) is formed from the plasma membrane (*neurilemma*) of the neurolemmal or Schwann cells (Fig. 142). The myelin sheath begins a short distance distal to the axon hillock. The sheath can be distinguished in light microscopy with fat stains. Axons enclosed in a myelin sheath are called *myelinated fibers;* conversely those axons without a myelin sheath are called *un-myelinated fibers* (Figs. 145, 146, 149, and 150).

The myelin sheath is formed by a spiral infolding and fusion of the neurilemma of the Schwann cells in the peripheral nerves (Fig. 142). The sheath has an appearance analogous to a jelly roll. The exact kinetics of formation of the myelin sheath are unknown, but it is felt to be a spiraling growth of the Schwann cell, rather than a rotation of axon or Schwann cell about each other. Each myelin lamellae is about 130 to 180 Ångstroms thick (Fig. 150). In unmyelinated cells the infolding of the neurilemma does not produce two fused plasma membranes as in the formation of myelin, but remains visible as two unit membranes (75 Ångstroms thick) separated by a clear space (gap substance) about 150 Ångstroms wide (Fig. 145). The gap substance is continuous with the extracellular space. Myelinated fibers transmit impulses faster than unmyelinated fibers.

Points of oblique discontinuities (*Schmidt-Lanterman* or *incision clefts*) can be found irregularly placed along the myelin sheath in in vitro tissue culture preparations as well as in electron microscopic preparations. The Schmidt-Lanterman clefts probably represent a shearing defect in the myelin sheath.

Each Schwann cell completely surrounds the axons except in the areas where the initial infolding of the neurilemma (*mesaxon*) forms the myelin sheath (Fig. 145). The cell en-

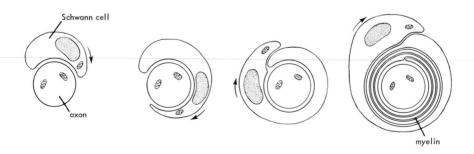

Fig. 142. Schematic representation of myelin formation by Schwann cell growth about axon. (Modified and redrawn from: B. (Geren) Uzman, Exper. Cell Research **7:**560, 1954.)

closes a single axon in myelinated fibers and multiple axons in unmyelinated fibers (Figs. 145, 149). It has an oval nucleus and the usual cell organelles. Schwann cells are identified by their association with axons and myelin rather than by any distinctive fine structural features.

At the junction of Schwann cells (*node of Ranvier*) the axon is thinned, the myelin sheath is absent, and the axon is covered by only a thin portion of Schwann cell cytoplasm and axolemma (Fig. 154). With the electron microscope the myelin sheath appears to be "unwrapped" at the node of Ranvier. Nodes of Ranvier are located at regular intervals along the myelinated fibers of both the peripheral and the central nervous systems. The length of internodal segments varies with the location of the fibers. Collateral branches of the nerve fibers originate at the nodes of Ranvier. Depolarization and repolarization occur only in the area of the nodes where the myelin sheath is absent, and the impulse "jumps" from one cell to another, a process known as *saltatory conduction*.

NEUROGLIAL (GLIAL) CELLS

Three distinct neuroglial (glial) cells can be distinguished: astroglia or astrocytes, oligodendroglia or oligocytes, and microglia or microcytes. The *astrocytes* ("spider cells") form a supporting network between neurons and surround blood vessels with dichotomous cytoplasmic processes (*pedicles*). With the light microscope two types of astrocytes are found. One type, the *fibrous astrocyte*, which has numerous thin processes is abundant in the white matter of the cortex; and the other, the *protoplasmic astrocyte*, which has a granular cytoplasm and thick processes is found in the gray matter. The most striking features of astrocytes are their abundant cytoplasm and numerous thin cytoplasmic filaments (about 75 Ångstroms in diameter) coursing randomly through the cytoplasm. Fibrous astrocytes have a more regular contour than protoplasmic astrocytes which are extremely irregular. Mitochondria of astrocytes are larger

than those of neurons and other glial cells. Astrocytes function in inflammation and repair, and it has been theorized that they also function in water and ion exchange in the central nervous system.

The *oligocyte* is the central nervous system homologue of the Schwann cell. It contains the usual cytoplasmic organelles, but it is distinguished by a sparsity of ergastoplasm, many free ribosomes, lack of cytoplasmic fibrils, and a small round nucleus (Fig. 144). The oligocytes of the gray matter frequently are found surrounding neurons forming perineuronal satellites, or in columns or rows about nerve fibers. Functionally and morphologically in light microscopy, oligocytes of the white matter differ from those in the vicinity of neurons but positive differential fine structural characteristics of these two cells have yet to be described. The oligocyte of the white matter seems to be concerned principally with the maintenance and synthesis of myelin (myelinogenesis) in the normal state and with the disposal of myelin in certain pathological conditions. Because of the increase in oligocyte cytoplasm with cerebral edema and contraction of cytoplasm with dehydration, the oligocyte has been implicated in fluid transport in the central nervous system.

Microcytes, which are motile and phagocytic, are the scavengers of the nervous system, and are analogous to the reticuloendothelial cells of other areas of the body (see Chap. 15). Numerous cisternae of ergastoplasm, vacuoles, a well-developed Golgi material, and phagocytosed inclusions are found in the cytoplasm.

SYNAPSES

Synapses are the sites of morphological contact that function to transmit impulses from one neuron to another (Figs. 147, 148, 151 to 153, and 155). The main features of synapses have been known for many years. On the basis of light microscopic studies, neurocytologists postulated the existence of three main types of synapse: axodentric, axoaxonic, and asoxomatic (neuromuscular, etc.). Electron micro-

Fig. 143.

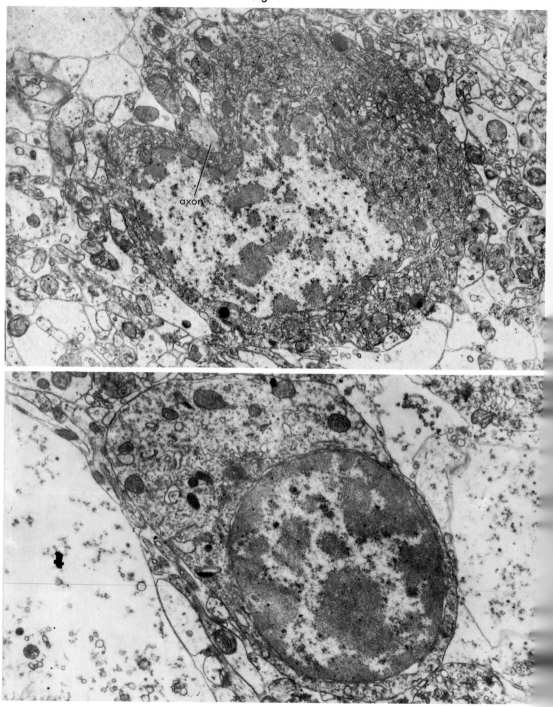

axon

Fig. 144.

Fig. 143. Cerebellar neuron with small part of axon visible. Dog. × 19,000.

Fig. 144. Oligocyte. Dog cerebellum. × 17,000.

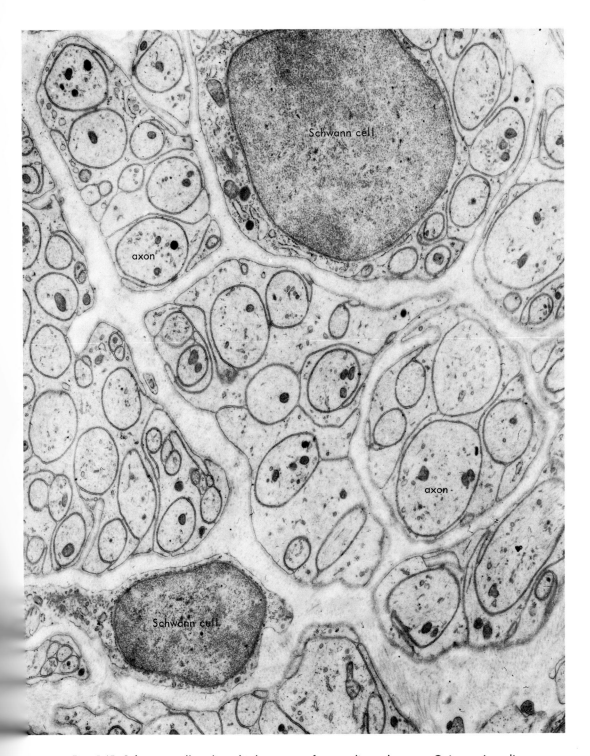

Fig. 145. Schwann cell with multiple axons of unmyelinated nerve. Guinea pig salivary gland. $\times$ 9,000.

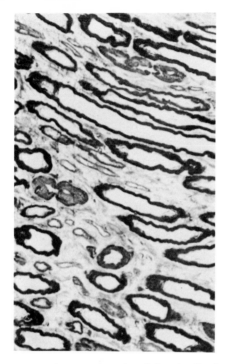

Fig. 146. Light micrograph of longitudinal and cross sections of myelin in sciatic nerve of dog. Compare with electron micrograph of Figure 149. Maraglas embedding, toluidine blue stain. × 200.

thickenings of the apposing plasma membranes resembling desmosomes.

Where an axon is in contact with a muscle myofibril (*neuromuscular junction*), it has the same presynaptic bouton structure as in the axodendritic synapse (Figs. 148 and 155). However, the postsynaptic portion is composed of complicated infoldings (*junctional folds*) of the sarcolemma, forming troughs (Figs. 148 and 155). The trough is an extracellular space that contains basement membrane material. The Schwann cell sheath is thinned to a narrow envelope about the presynaptic bouton in this type of axosomatic synapse.

Synaptic transmission differs from nerve fiber transmission in being primarily chemical rather than electrical. Synaptic transmission is unidirectional, whereas conduction in either direction is possible in the nerve fiber. This property is believed to be due to the unidirectional release of neurohumoral (transmitter) substances located in the presynaptic vesicles, which can be brought about only by stimulation of the presynaptic axon. Once expelled into the extracellular gap, the transmitter substance is rapidly degraded by enzymatic action. Acetylcholine is a known transmitter substance; substances suspected of being transmitters are 5-hydroxytryptamine (serotonin), noradrenaline, and other substances

scopic studies have shown that the three different types of synapse have the same basic fine structure and organization (Figs. 47, 48, 153, and 155). The synapse consists of a presynaptic and postsynaptic portion. The presynaptic portion is a bulbous expansion (*bouton*) of the terminal portion of the axon (Figs. 147 and 148). The boutons measure 0.5 microns to more than 4 microns in diameter and are large enough to be visualized in the light microscope with appropriate stains. The presynaptic boutons are characterized by clusters of small, round and elongate mitochondria, and small vesicles (*synaptic vesicles*) 200 to 650 Ångstroms in diameter (Figs. 153 and 155). The mode of formation of these vesicles is unknown. Some presynaptic boutons contain filaments. The plasma membranes of the presynaptic and post-synaptic portions are separated by an extracellular space, *gap*, about 200 Ångstroms wide. At various points along the gap of separation there are dense local

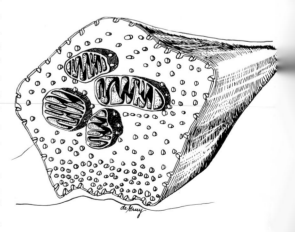

Fig. 147. Three-dimensional schematic representation of the bouton of axodendritic synapse.

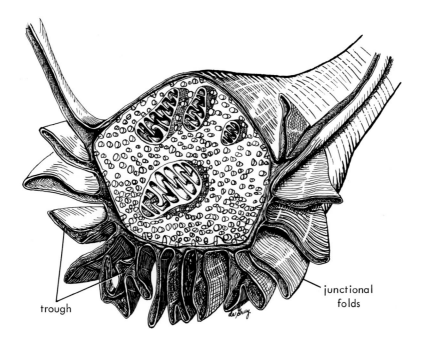

trough

junctional
folds

Fig. 148. Three-dimensional schematic representation of the bouton and troughs of neuromuscular junction.

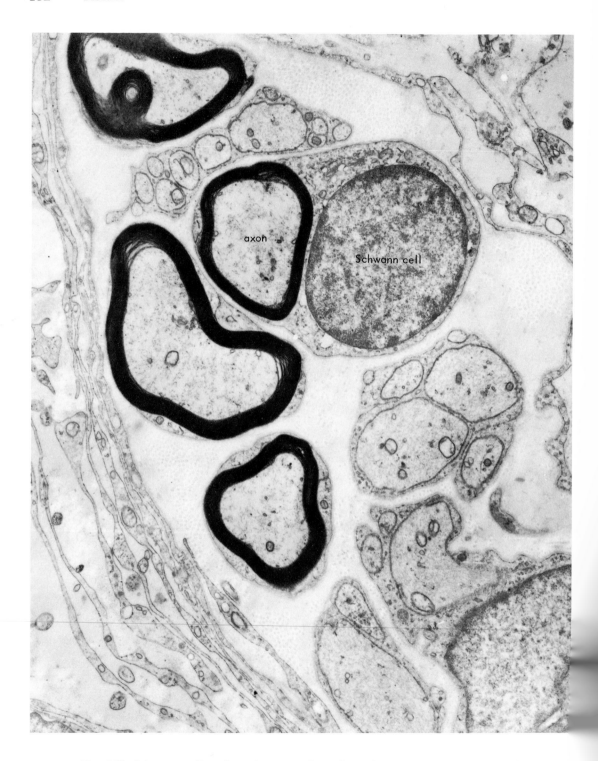

Fig. 149. Schwann cell and single axon of myelinated nerve. Rabbit ciliary body. $\times$ 15,000.

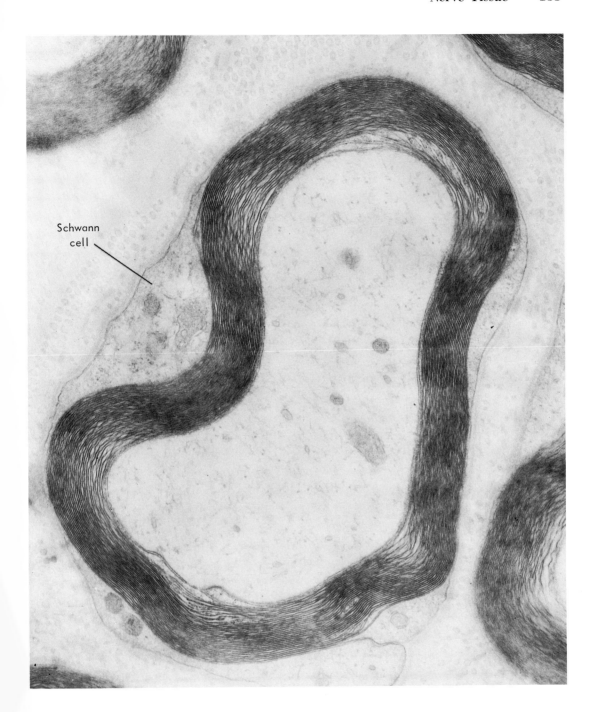

Schwann
cell

Fig. 150. Concentric lamellae of myelin. Dog sciatic nerve. $\times$ 43,000.

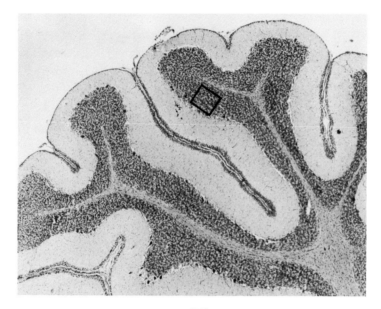

Fig. 151.

Fig. 151. Light micrograph of cerebellum of dog. The boxed area is comparable to electron micrograph of Figure 152. Hematoxylin and eosin stain. $\times$ 33.

Fig. 152. Synapses. Dog cerebellum. $\times$ 11,000.

Fig. 153. Axodendritic synapses. Dog cerebral cortex. $\times$ 20,000.

Fig. 152.

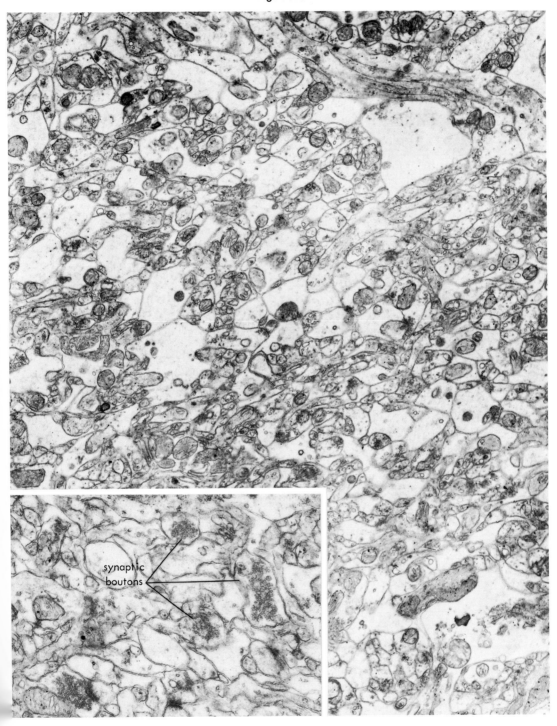

Fig. 153.

Fig. 154. Node of Ranvier. Dog sciatic nerve. $\times$ 20,000.

Fig. 155. Neuromuscular junction. Rat skeletal (extraocular) muscle. $\times$ 23,000.

Fig. 154.

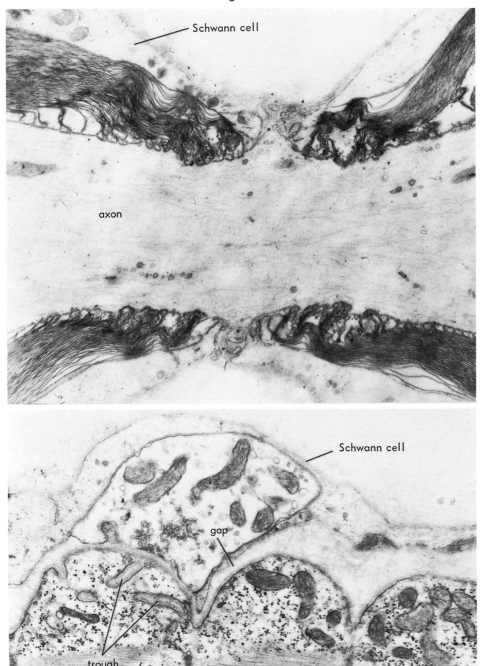

Fig. 155.

yet to be characterized. Acetylcholinesterase, associated with the plasma membranes of the synapse, produces enzymatic degradation of the acetylcholine.

REFERENCES

ANDERSSON-CEDERGREN, E.: Ultrastructure of motor end plate and sarcoplasmic components of mouse skeletal muscle fiber as revealed by three-dimensional reconstructions from serial sections. J. Ultrast. Res., Suppl. 1, 1959.

BUNGE, R., M. BUNGE and H. RIS: Ultrastructural study of remyelination in an experimental lesion in adult cat spinal cord. J. Biophys. Biochem. Cytol., 10:67–94, 1961.

CAUSEY, G.: *The Cell of Schwann,* E. & S. Livingstone, Ltd., London, 1960.

DE ROBERTIS, E.: Submicroscopic morphology of the snyapse. Intern. Rev. Cytol. 8:61–96, 1959.

DUNCAN, D. Personal communication.

ELFVIN, L.: The ultrastructure of the nodes of Ranvier in cat sympathetic nerve fibers. J. Ultrast. Res., 5:374–387, 1961.

ENGSTRÖM, H., and J. WERSALL: Myelin sheath structure in nerve fiber demyelinization and branching regions. Exper. Cell Res., 14:414–425, 1958.

FERNÁNDEZ-MORÁN, H.: Cell membrane ultrastructure: Low-temperature electron microscopy and x-ray diffraction studies of lipoprotein components in lamellar systems, in *Ultrastructure and Metabolism of the Nervous System,* edited by S. Korey, A. Pope and E. Robins, 235–267. The Williams and Wilkins Company, Baltimore, 1962.

FINEAN, J.: *Chemical Ultrastructure in Living Tissues,* pp. 75–82. Charles C Thomas, Springfield, 1961.

GEREN, B.: The formation of myelin from the Schwann cell surface in peripheral nerves of chick embryos. Exper. Cell Res., 7:558–562, 1954.

GERSCHENFELD, H., F. WELD, J. ZADUNAISKY, and E. DE ROBERTIS: Function of astroglia in the water-ion metabolism of the central nervous system. Neurol., 9:412–425, 1959.

GRAY, E.: Ultrastructure of synapses of the cerebral cortex and of certain specializations of neuroglial membranes, in *Electron Microscopy in Anatomy,* edited by J. Boyd, F. Johnson, and J. Lever, pp. 54–73. The Williams and Wilkins Company, Baltimore, 1961.

HAMBERGER, A., and H. HYDÉN: Inverse enzymatic changes in neurons and glia during increased function and hypoxia. J. Cell Biol., 16:521–526, 1963.

HERNDON, R.: The fine structure of the Purkinje cell. J. Cell Biol., 18:167–180, 1963.

HYDÉN, H.: The neuron, in *The Cell,* vol. IV, edited by J. Brachet and A. Mirsky, pp. 216–323. Academic Press, Inc., New York, 1961.

LUSE, S.: Ultrastructure of the brain and its relation to transport of metabolites, in *Ultrastructure and Metabolism of the Nervous System,* edited by S. Korey, A. Pope, and E. Robins, pp. 1–26. The Williams and Wilkins Company, Baltimore, 1962.

PALAY, S. and G. PALADE: The fine structure of neurons. J. Biophys. Biochem. Cytol., 1:69–88, 1955.

PETERS, A.: The formation and structure of myelin sheaths in the central nervous system. J. Biophys. Biochem. Cytol., 8:431–446, 1960.

REGER, J.: The fine structure of neuromuscular junctions and the sarcoplasmic reticulum of extrinsic eye muscles of *Fundulus heteroclitus.* J. Cell Biol., Suppl., 10:111–122, 1961.

ROBERTSON, J.: The ultrastructure of Schmidt-Lanterman clefts and related shearing defects of the myelin sheath. J. Biophys. Biochem. Cytol., 4:39–46, 1958.

SCHULTZ, R. and D. PEASE: Cicatrix formation in rat cerebral cortex as revealed by electron microscopy. Amer. J. Path., 35:1017–1041, 1959.

WHITTAKER, V. and E. GRAY: The synapse: Biology and morphology. Brit. Med. Bull., 18:223–228, 1962.

18

CONNECTIVE TISSUE:
LOOSE CONNECTIVE TISSUE

Loose connective tissue is a most important tissue in the body, yet it is a tissue about which much is to be learned. Advances in chemical methodology in the past few years have provided a wealth of data about chemical composition, but we still know little about the cellular origin and maintenance of the extracellular components of connective tissue.

Loose connective tissue is composed of fibrillar elements, certain cells, and an amorphous interstitial matrix known as cement or *ground substance* (Figs. 156 and 157). Connective tissue matrix cements the cells and tissues together in a fashion analogous to that in which mortar holds together the bricks in a building. The connective tissue not only affords tensile strength and a degree of mechanical stability, but it also fills the interstices between other tissue and vessels, and is intricately interwoven as a continuous structure throughout the body. If a cell could migrate through the continuous network of loose connective tissue, it potentially could travel throughout the entire body, in a fashion similar to the migration of a blood cell through the circulatory system.

COLLAGEN FIBERS

Collagen, the principal fibrous protein of connective tissue, appears in light microscopic studies as broad, wavy, ribbon-like bands that stain with acidophilic dyes. With the electron microscope the large bands of collagen are composed of aggregates of smaller fibers known as *unit fibers* (Fig. 158). The unit fiber of collagen has an axial periodic structure repeating every 640 Ångstroms (Fig. 158). The periodic structure can be varied between 500 and 3,000 Ångstroms in collagen fibers that have been dissolved and reconstituted in vitro. Most investigators favor the concept that collagen is formed extracellularly by the polymerization or growing of a prefibrillar protein (*tropocollagen*) which is elaborated by a cell, usually a fibroblast.

ELASTIC FIBERS

Elastic fibers are broad, refractile fibers that can be stained with virtually all histologic stains. As the name implies, they have the property of resilience. In electron microscopic studies elastic fibers appear as broad ribbons of moderate electron density that lack periodic banding (Figs. 160, 165, and 167). Tiny fibrils (*microfibrils*) are seen at the margin of the elastic fibers (Fig. 160).

In medium sized arteries the intima is composed of endothelial cells and elastic fibers which appear as an amorphous membrane of varying, but usually low density (internal elastic membrane) (Figs. 165 and 166). In larger arteries the elastic membrane frequently

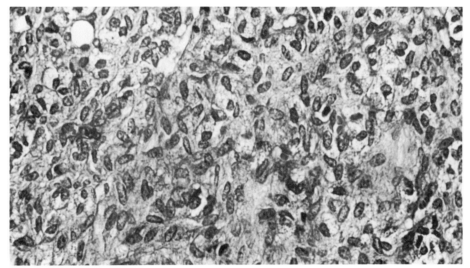

Fig. 156.

Fig. 156. Light micrograph of loose connective tissue of dog ovarian stroma. Compare with electron micrograph of Figure 157. Hematoxylin and eosin stain. × 375.

Fig. 157. Low magnification of collagen and fibroblasts in loose connective tissue. Dog ovarian stoma. × 3,300.

Fig. 158. Collagen bundles showing periodic banding. Dermis of dog eyelid. × 7,400.

Fig. 157.

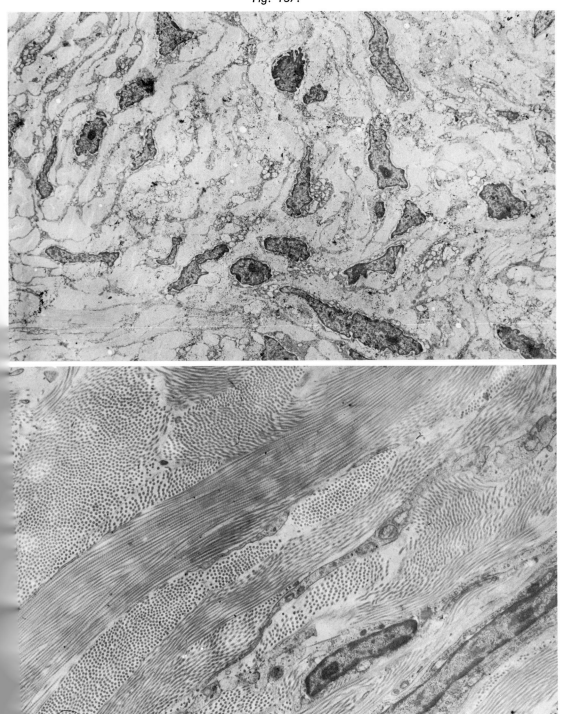

Fig. 158.

Fig. 159. Fibroblast of lamina propria. Rabbit ciliary body. $\times$ 16,000.

Fig. 160. Elastic fibers with microfibrils visible at periphery of fibers. Dog tracheal lamina propria. $\times$ 9,800.

Fig. 161. Reticular fibers surrounding capillary. Rat ileal lamina propria. $\times$ 7,800.

Fig. 162. Basement membrane material surrounding capillary endothelial cell and pericyte (*Rouget cell*). Dog cerebral cortex. $\times$ 14,000.

Fig. 159.

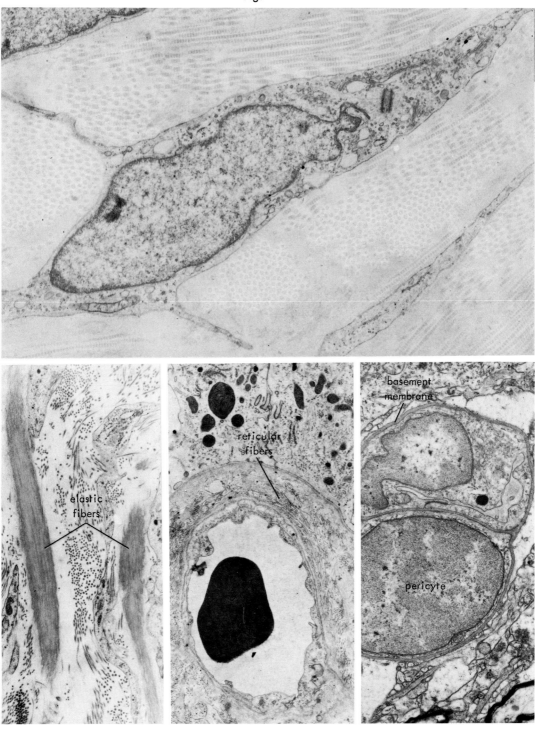

Fig. 160.   Fig. 161.   Fig. 162.

Fig. 163. Histiocyte (*macrophage*) with phagocytosed inclusions. Compare with monocyte of Figure 182. Lamina propria of dog gall bladder. $\times$ 11,000.

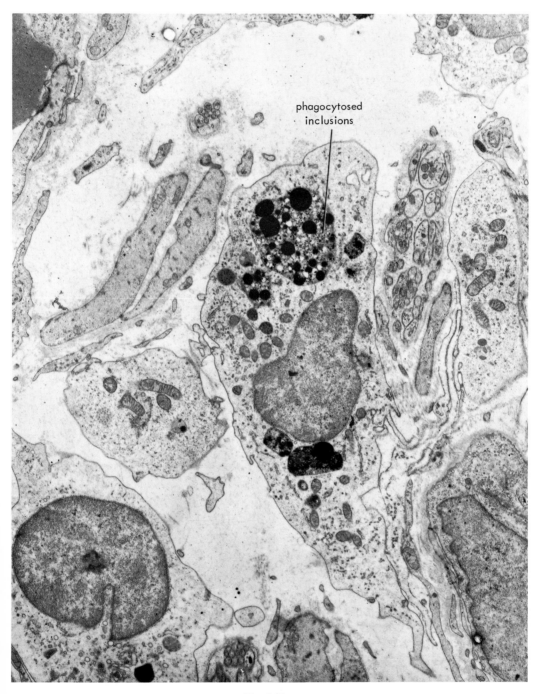

phagocytosed
inclusions

Fig. 163.

is split or is associated with collagen fibers (Fig. 166).

Elastic fibers are composed of a protein substance, *elastin*. The cell that elaborates elastin is not known.

RETICULAR FIBERS

Reticular fibers represent a third fibrillar component of connective tissue visible with the light microscope, and are identifiable by their reaction with silver stains. The identity of these fibers as a third distinct fibrillar element is not established with certainty by use of the electron microscope. Some purport that reticular fibers are small collagen fibers since collagen fibers stain brown with the same silver stain that colors reticular fibers black in light microscopic preparations. Present evidence favors the interpretation that reticular fibers are basement membrane substance or basement membrane substance containing unit fibers of collagen (Fig. 161). In either case, reticular fibers may not represent a third chemically definable fibrous protein, but rather are a combination or special form of other components of connective tissue.

FIBROBLASTS

It is difficult to define constant cellular components of connective tissue because of its changing cell picture as evidenced by the fact that under certain circumstances any cell of the blood may be seen in connective tissue. The most constant, but not invariable, cell in connective tissue is the fibroblast. The fibroblast is an elongate, fusiform cell that is seen best in light microscopic studies with an iron hematoxylin stain; it is difficult to see the thin filaments of cytoplasm on either side of the nucleus in hematoxylin and eosin stained sections (Fig. 156). In electron micrographs the fibroblast usually is an elongate cell with a fusiform nucleus (Figs. 157 and 159). The usual cytoplasmic organelles are found in the cytoplasm near the poles of the nucleus. The ergastoplasm (rough-surfaced endoplasmic reticulum) appears as dilated sacs or cisternae

containing a moderately dense material presumed to be a precursor substance of the matrix and the fibrillar elements of connective tissue (Fig. 159). The fibroblast is generally conceded to be responsible for the deposition and maintenance of loose connective tissue. However, connective tissue matrix and fibrillar elements are abundant in the media of large arteries where only smooth muscle cells are found (Figs. 165 and 167). Whether smooth muscle cells, or cells other than fibroblasts, have the capacity to elaborate some of the components of connective tissue remains to be determined.

UNDIFFERENTIATED CELLS

Reticulum cells and undifferentiated mesenchymal cells have been described in loose connective tissue, but a clear definition of these cells is lacking as to source, structure, and function. Fibroblasts are related to these cells embryologically, but any other relationships remain unproven.

MAST CELLS

Mast cells may be present in loose connective tissue. As seen with the light microscope these cells are ovoid, about 15 microns in diameter, and have large cytoplasmic granules which are best visualized with special stains such as toluidine blue or thionine. The mast cell closely resembles the basophilic leukocyte (see Chap. 20). In electron microscopic studies the mast cell is found to have all the usual cytoplasmic organelles in addition to the large dense cytoplasmic granules. Heparin and histamine have been isolated from the granules.

HISTIOCYTES

Histiocytes are large phagocytic mononuclear cells that are referred to by a variety of names: adventitial cells, wandering cells, macrophages, and clasmatocytes. They are best identified by introducing foreign material, such as thorium dioxide, carbon particles, or trypan blue, which is phagocytosed by the histiocytes but not by the fibroblast. Histiocytes usually are larger than fibroblasts, have an irregular shape, and an ovoid nucleus with considerable cytoplasm (Fig. 163). In the spleen, liver, and certain other tissues, there are "fixed" histiocytes; these cells, together with the histiocytes of connective tissue, comprise the reticuloendothelial system. Interrelationships of endothelial cells, blood monocytes, and histiocytes have been postulated but still remain to be proven (see Chap. 20).

MISCELLANEOUS CELLS

Under certain conditions lymphocytes, eosinophilic leukocytes, plasma cells, erythrocytes, and neutrophilic leukocytes migrate into loose connective tissue. Most such conditions represent pathologic changes.

MATRIX

The amorphous matrix of loose connective tissue is not well differentiated with ordinary histologic stains (Fig. 156). It is composed of mucoproteins (proteins combined with hyaluronic acid or chondroitin sulfate), glycoproteins (proteins combined with sialic acid, etc.), and other complex macromolecules yet to be characterized. The composition of the amorphous matrix varies in different anatomic locations but usually is characteristic for each location. In electron micrographs, also, the matrix is not well differentiated (Figs. 157 and 167). Only the basement membrane is visible as a moderately dense zone adjacent to the plasma membrane of cells (Figs. 162, 168, 169, and 172). This membrane is found along the basal surface of epithelial cells and surrounding some cells of mesodermal origin such as pericytes and smooth muscle cells, with the exception of blood cells (Figs. 162, 164, and 168).

The basement membrane is the only constant layer of capillaries, except sinusoids, throughout the body. Capillary basement membranes usually range from 200 to 500 Ångstroms in thickness, except the basement

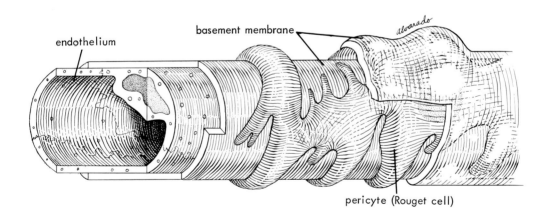

endothelium

basement membrane

alvarado

pericyte (Rouget cell)

Fig. 164. Three-dimensional cutaway schematic representation of basement membrane substance surrounding pericyte *(Rouget cell)* as well as capillary endothelial cell.

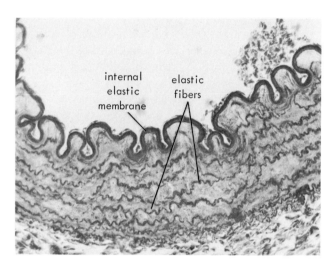

internal
elastic
membrane

elastic
fibers

Fig. 165.

Fig. 165. Light micrograph of a portion of guinea pig aorta. Compare with electron micrographs of aorta (Figures 166 and 167). Elastic-van Gieson stain. $\times$ 540.

Fig. 166. Internal elastic membrane. Intima of dog aorta. $\times$ 5,600.

Fig. 167. Elastic fibers, collagen fibers, and smooth muscle cells. Media of dog aorta. $\times$ 4,100.

Fig. 166.

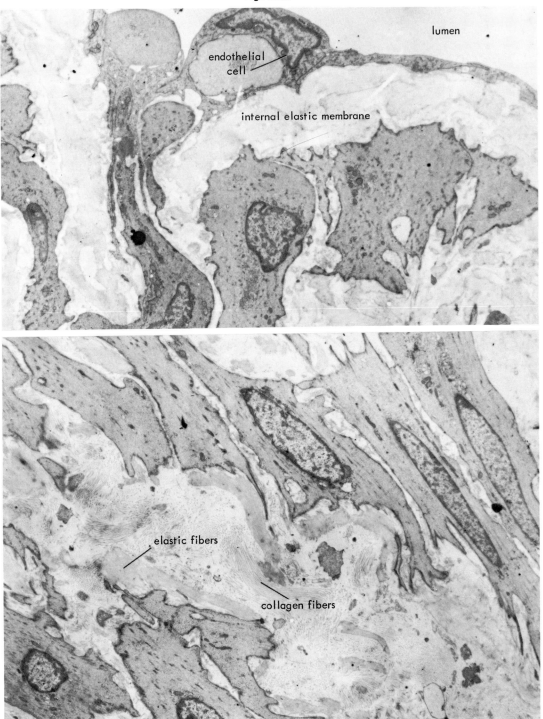

Fig. 167.

Fig. 168. Basement membrane material surrounding vascular endothelium and pericyte (*Rouget cell*). Rat skeletal (*extraocular*) muscle. $\times$ 19,000.

Fig. 169. Basement membrane of contracted arteriole. Dog dorsal root ganglion. $\times$ 13,000.

Fig. 168.

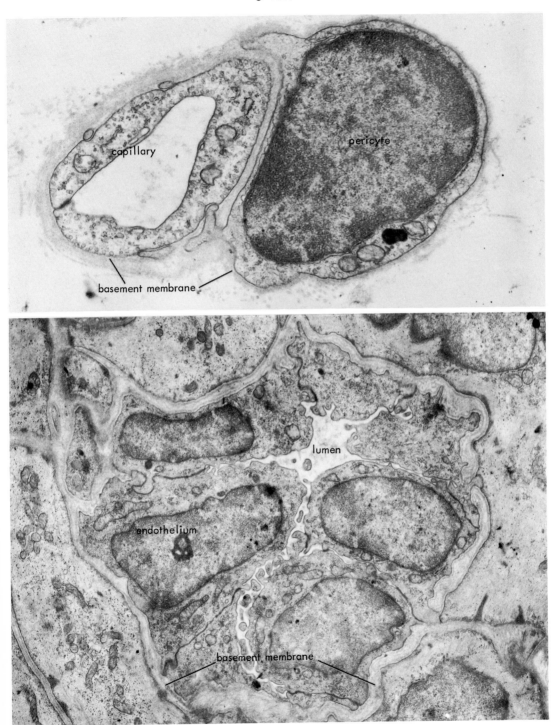

Fig. 169.

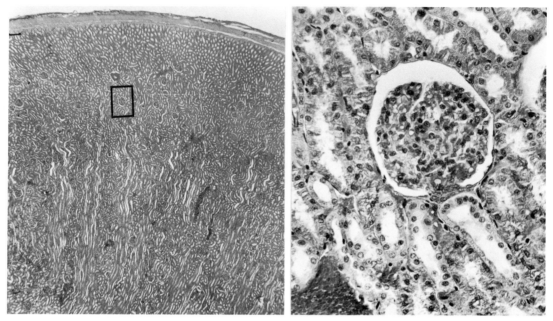

Fig. 170.   Fig. 171.

Fig. 170. Light micrograph of rat kidney cortex. Boxed area is shown in Figure 171. Hematoxylin and eosin stain. $\times$ 30.

Fig. 171. Light micrograph of a kidney glomerulus. Rat. Compare with electron micrograph of Figure 172. Hematoxylin and eosin stain. $\times$ 480.

Fig. 172. Basement membrane of glomerulus is thicker than capillary basement membranes found elsewhere. Basement membrane substance entirely underlies endothelial cells but frequently is incomplete over mesangial (*axial*) cell. Occasionally collagen fibers can be found in extracellular space about mesangial "stalk." Rat kidney. $\times$ 8,100.

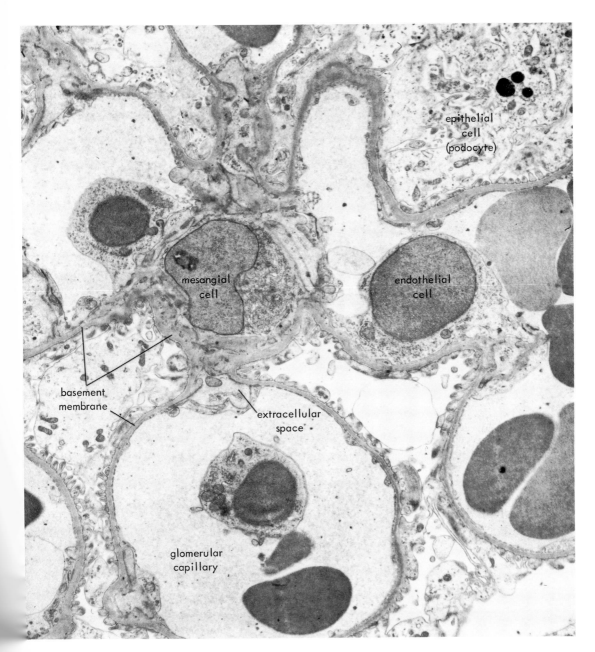

Fig. 172.

membrane of glomerular capillaries which is considerably thicker (Figs. 164, 167, 169, and 172). In areas where vascular endothelium is absent or fenestrated, the basement membrane constitutes the only physical barrier to transportation of substances across the vascular wall. The true role that the basement membrane plays in capillary permeability is yet to be determined.

The basement membrane probably represents an increased concentration of amorphous matrix. However, its complete chemical composition is unknown.

REFERENCES

BANFIELD, W.: Collagen and reticulin, in *Frontiers of Cytology*, edited by S. Palay, pp. 504–519. Yale University Press, New Haven, 1958.

BROWN, A., and J. MENKART: Physical, chemical, and mechanical properties of protein fibers, in *Ultrastructure of Protein Fibers*, edited by R. Borasky, pp. 5–17. Academic Press, Inc., New York, 1963.

CHAPMAN, J.: Fibroblasts and collagen. Brit. Med. Bull., **18**:233–237, 1962.

CHARLES, A.: Human elastic fibers. Electron microscopic appearances of the elastic fibers of human skin in thin section. Brit. J. Derm., **73**:57–60, 1961.

DORFMAN, A., and S. SCHILLER: Mucopolysaccharides of connective tissue, in *Biological Structure and Function,* vol. I, edited by T. Goodwin and O. Lindberg, pp. 327–340. Academic Press, Inc., New York, 1961.

FRITTON-JACKSON, S., and R. SMITH: Studies on the biosynthesis of collagen. 1. The growth of fowl osteoblasts and the formation of collagen in tissue culture. J. Biophys. Biochem. Cytol., **3**:897–912, 1957.

GROSS, J., J. HIGHBERGER, and F. SCHMITT: Collagen structures considered as states of aggregation of a kinetic unit. The tropocollagen particle. Proc. Nat. Acad. Sci., **56**:674–683, 1954.

NODA, H., and R. WYCKOFF: The electron microsscopy of reciprocated collagen. Biochim. Biophys. Acta, **7**:494–506, 1951.

PAHLKE, G.: Elektronenmikroskopische untersuchungen an der interzellular-substanz des menschlichen sehnengewebes. Ztschr. Zellforsch., **39**:421–430, 1954.

PORTER, K., and G. PAPPAS: Collagen formation by fibroblasts of the chick embryo dermis. J. Biophys. Biochem. Cytol., **5**:153–166, 1959.

RHODIN, J., and T. DALHAMN: Electron microscopy of collagen and elastin in lamina propria of the tracheal mucosa of rat. Exper. Cell Res., **9**:371–375, 1955.

Ross, R., and E. BENDITT: Wound healing and collagen formation. 2. Fine structure in experimental scurvy. J. Cell. Biol., **12**:533–551, 1962.

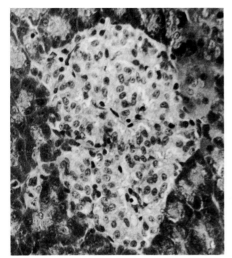

Fig. 173. Light micrograph of a pancreatic islet. Dog. Compare with electron micrograph of Figure 174. Hematoxylin and eosin stain. $\times$ 270.

Fig. 173.

Fig. 174. Contrary to common belief as a result of light microscopic studies, cells of the pancreatic islet (*islet of Langerhans*) can be found outside the loose connective tissue "capsule" of the islet. Dog pancreas. $\times$ 5,600.

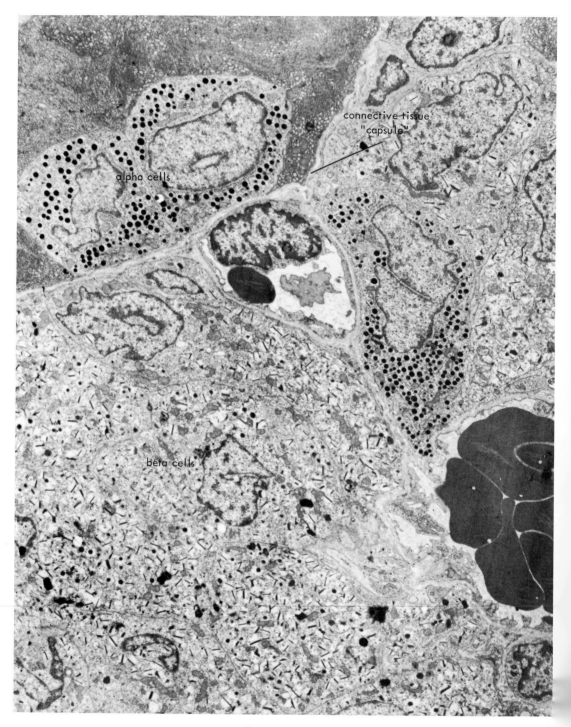

Fig. 174.

19

CONNECTIVE TISSUE:
CARTILAGE AND BONE

Cartilage and bone are forms of connective tissue that function primarily in mechanical support. Both have the same basic structural organization and elements as loose connective tissue, namely, cells, fibrillar elements, and an interstitial matrix (ground substance). Besides the function of support, cartilage forms a frame on which bone develops, and together with bone, participates in storage or metabolism of vitamins and minerals (calcium, phosphorus, magnesium, and sodium).

CELLS

The fine structure of cartilage cells, bone cells, and fibroblasts is similar; only the shape of these cells varies appreciably (Figs. 159 and 177). The differentiation of these cells in electron microscopy is largely dependent on their position and environment. Cartilage cells (*chondrocytes*) are usually found in groups as a result of multiple cell divisions after being trapped in a single lacuna by the extracellular elements of cartilage (Figs. 175 and 176). Chondrocytes usually have a spiny, irregular outline, except in articular cartilage where they have a fusiform shape similar to that of fibroblasts (Figs. 159 and 177). Bone cells (*osteocytes*) assume the oval or spindle shape of the lacuna in which they are found. *Osteo-*

blasts are recognized by their position on the surface of growing bone. *Osteoclasts* are associated with the resorption of bone. The most striking fine structural feature of all these cells is the well developed cisternal form of ergastoplasm (Fig. 177). Lipid droplets and variable amounts of glycogen are frequently prominent in chondrocytes (Fig. 177). The other usual cytoplasmic organelles are present.

FIBERS

The bulk of cartilage and bone is composed of extracellular elements. The fibrillar element of hyaline cartilage usually is not visible with the light microscope, but can be resolved with the electron microscope. The predominant fibrillar element is collagen. In certain types of cartilage, other connective tissue fibers, such as elastin in elastic cartilage, can be found. The randomly arranged unit collagen fibers surrounding chondrocytes measure about 200 Ångstroms in diameter, and their periodic structure is either lacking or ill defined (Fig. 178). Occasionally a periodicity of 210 Ångstroms is visible. In articular cartilage the fibers have a larger diameter and have the 640 Ångstroms axial periodicity characteristic of mature collagen. Autoradiographic studies and other evidence suggest that both the fibrillar

177

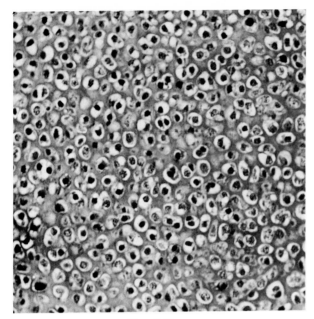

Fig. 175.

Fig. 175. Light micrograph of fetal cartilage of knee joint. Mouse. The lacunae are the result of tissue shrinkage during processing. Compare with electron micrograph of Figure 176. Hematoxylin and eosin stain. $\times$ 345.

Fig. 176. Fetal cartilage of knee joint. Mouse. $\times$ 15,000.

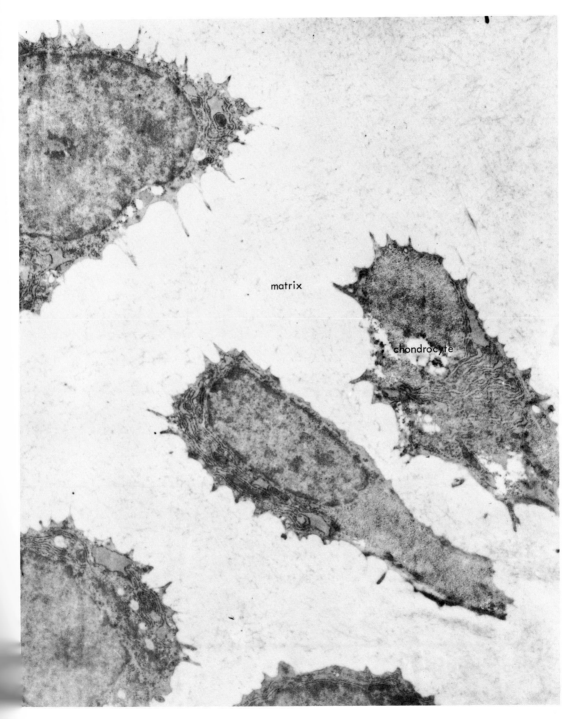

Fig. 176.

Fig. 177. Chondrocyte of fetal cartilage of knee joint. Mouse. Note resemblance of fine structure of chondrocyte to that of fibroblast (Figure 159). $\times$ 23,000.

Fig. 178. Fibrillar component of fetal cartilage of knee joint. Mouse. Note absence of axial periodicity. $\times$ 25,000.

Fig. 179. The collagen fibers of bone, with periodic banding, are barely visible within the calcified matrix. Human. $\times$ 23,000.

Fig. 177.

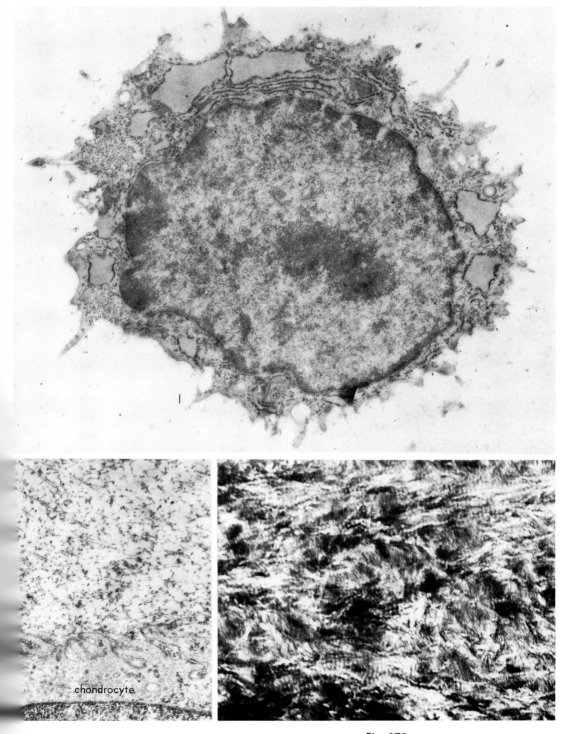

chondrocyte

Fig. 178.   Fig. 179.

element and the interstitial matrix are elaborated by the cells.

MATRIX

The interstitial matrix surrounding the fibrillar elements of both bone and cartilage is not well understood. The matrix is composed of mucopolysaccharide, protein, water, tropocollagen, and substances yet to be characterized. In electron micrographs the matrix appears homogeneous with moderate density (Figs. 176 and 178). Because cartilage is devoid of blood vessels it is thought that nutrients from the blood pass freely through the matrix to reach the cells.

Although basic similarities of calcification (ossification, mineralization) of bone and cartilage exist, there are significant structural as well as chemical differences. Capillary invasion and cell degeneration precedes the ossification process. When mineralization of bone occurs, an amorphous substance clouds the interstitial matrix and apatite crystals ($Ca_{10}(PO_4)_6(OH)_2$) form. With electron diffraction studies it has been shown that the amorphous substance is apatite in a noncrystalline form. Apatite crystals are deposited first in relation to the interband region of each axial periodic band of the collagen fibers. Further crystallization apparently occurs spontaneously and randomly. Apatite crystals develop both in and on the collagen fibers, with eventual orientation of the crystals parallel to the long axes of the fibers (Fig. 179). Apatite formation in cartilage occurs randomly without orientation of the crystals.

REFERENCES

Cartilage

CAMERON, D., and R. ROBINSON: Electron microscopy of epiphyseal and articular cartilage matrix in the femur of the newborn infant. J. Bone & Joint Surg., 40:163–170, 1958.

GODMAN, G., and K. PORTER: Chondrogenesis, studied with the electron microscope. J. Biophys. Biochem. Cytol., 8:719–760, 1960.

KNESE, K., and A. KNOOP: Chondrogenese und osteogenese. Elektronenmikroskopische und lichtmikroskopische untersuchungen. Ztschr. Zellforsch., 55:412–468, 1961.

SHELDON, H., and R. ROBINSON: Studies on cartilage. Electron microscope observations on normal rabbit ear cartilage. J. Biophys. Biochem. Cytol., 4:401–406, 1958.

ZELANDER, T. Ultrastructure of articular cartilage. Ztschr. Zellforsch., 49:720–738, 1959.

Bone

CAMERON, D.: The fine structure of osteoblasts in the metaphysis of the tibia of the young rat. J. Biophys. Biochem. Cytol., 9:583–595, 1961.

DUDLEY, R., and D. SPIRO: The fine structure of bone cells. J. Biophys. Biochem. Cytol., 11:627–649, 1961.

FRITTON-JACKSON, S: Fibrogenesis and the formation of matrix, in *Bone as a Tissue*, edited by K. Rodahl, J. Nicholson, and E. Brown, pp. 165–185. McGraw-Hill Book Company, New York, 1960.

GERSH, I.: Ground substance and calcification, in *Bone as a Tissue*, edited by K. Rodahl, J. Nicholson, and E. Brown, pp. 128–143. McGraw-Hill Book Company, New York, 1960.

KNESE, K., and A. KNOOP: Uber der ort der bildung des mukopolysaccharidproteinkomplexes inknorpelgewebe. Elektronenmikroskopische und histochemische untersuchungen. Ztschr. Zellforsch., 53:201–258, 1961.

LACROIX, P.: Bone and cartilage, in *The Cell*, Vol. V, edited by J. Brachet and A. Mirsky, pp. 219–266. Academic Press, Inc., New York 1961.

ROBINSON, R., and H. SHELDON: Crystal-collagen relationships in healing rickets, in *Calcification in Biological Systems*, edited by R. Sognnaes, pp. 261–279. American Association for the Advancement of Science, Publication 64, Washington, 1960.

20

CONNECTIVE TISSUE:
BLOOD AND BONE MARROW

BLOOD

Foremost among the many functions of blood are the nutrition of tissues, removal of cellular waste products, and tissue defense. The fluid intercellular portion of blood (*plasma*) carries waste products and nutrients either in solution or in colloid suspension. Of the cellular elements (*corpuscles*), the red blood corpuscles (*erythrocytes*) carry nutrient oxygen to the tissues, while the white blood corpuscles (*leukocytes*) function primarily in tissue defense mechanisms. Erythrocytes spend their life span in the plasma where their function is performed. However, the plasma is merely a place of temporary sojourn for leukocytes since they arise, usually function, and die outside the blood stream.

Mature erythrocytes do not possess a nucleus and hence, are not true cells; leukocytes are true cells (Fig. 180). Leukocytes may be subdivided into granular forms (granulocytes: neutrophils, eosinophils, and basophils) and agranular forms (agranulocytes: monocytes and lymphocytes).

Erythrocytes

Mature erythrocytes are biconcave discs. The dense, homogeneous cytoplasm seen in electron micrographs is a result of the iron-containing hemoglobin (Figs. 183 and 184).

Immature erythrocytes (*reticulocytes*) have a reticulated structure when seen with the light microscope after supravital staining. With the electron microscope the reticulated appearance is seen to be a result of persistence of portions of endoplasmic reticulum and mitochondria (Fig. 183). The iron in hemoglobin normally is not visible in mature erythrocytes; however, in certain hemolytic diseases, non-hemoglobin iron (*ferritin*) can be seen in the cytoplasm.

Neutrophils

Neutrophils, the most numerous of the blood leukocytes, have a polymorphous (many lobed) nucleus that usually consists of three to five lobes connected by fine threads of nucleoplasm (Fig. 180). The cytoplasm contains granules 0.2 to 0.6 microns in diameter, which are neutrophilic using light microscopic techniques (i.e., they stain neutral with the Romanowsky compound, and acidic with Wright's stain). As seen with the electron microscope the granules are homogeneous and are surrounded by a membrane (Fig. 183). In mature neutrophils few mitochondria are present (Fig. 181). Neutrophils, capable of rapid ameboid movement, function as microphagocytes in the reaction to injury.

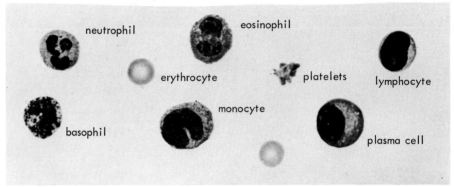

Fig. 180.

Fig. 180. Light micrograph of human blood cells. Compare with electron micrographs of Figures 181, 182, and 186. Wright's stain. $\times$ 2,200.

Fig. 181. Granulocytes. Basophil and neutrophil of dog; eosinophil of rat. $\times$ 14,000.

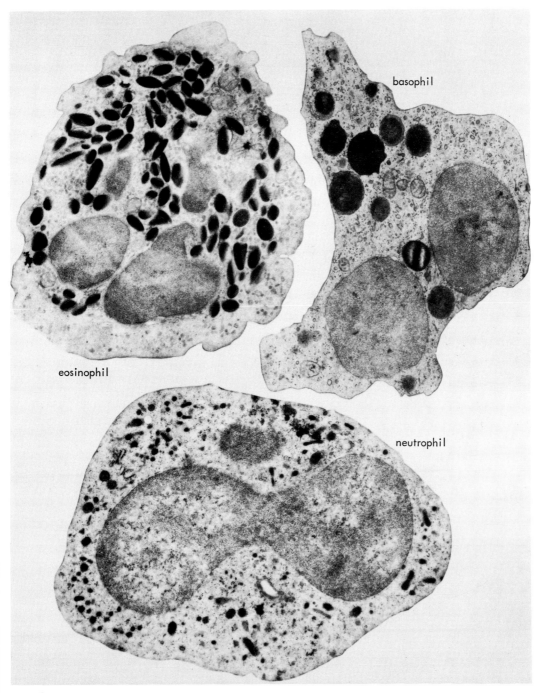

Fig. 181.

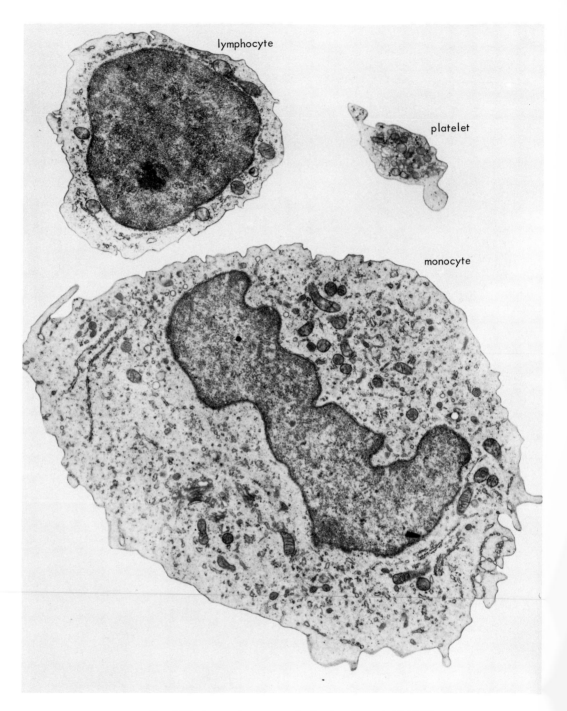

Fig. 182. Agranulocytes and platelet. Dog. $\times$ 14,000.

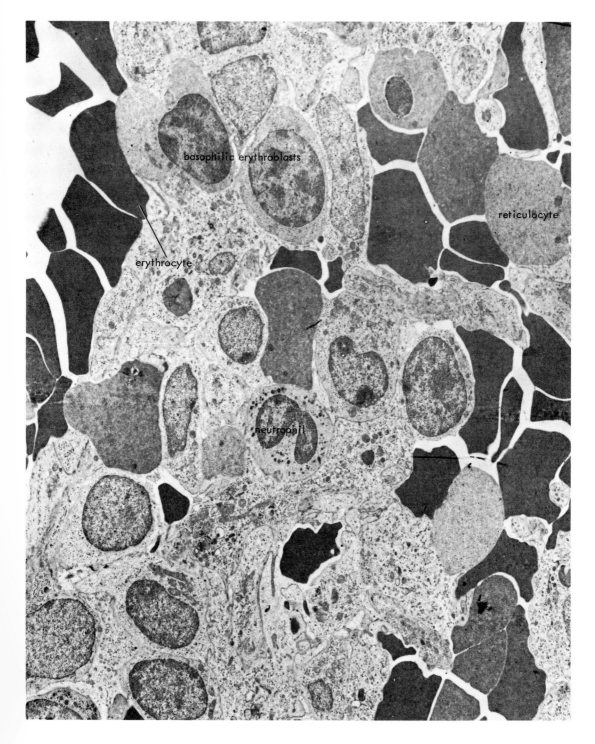

Fig. 183. Pulp cord containing mature and immature erythroid and myeloid cells. Dog spleen. $\times$ 4,100. (Reproduced from B. Galindo and J. Freeman, Anat. Rec., **147**:31, 1963.)

Fig. 184.

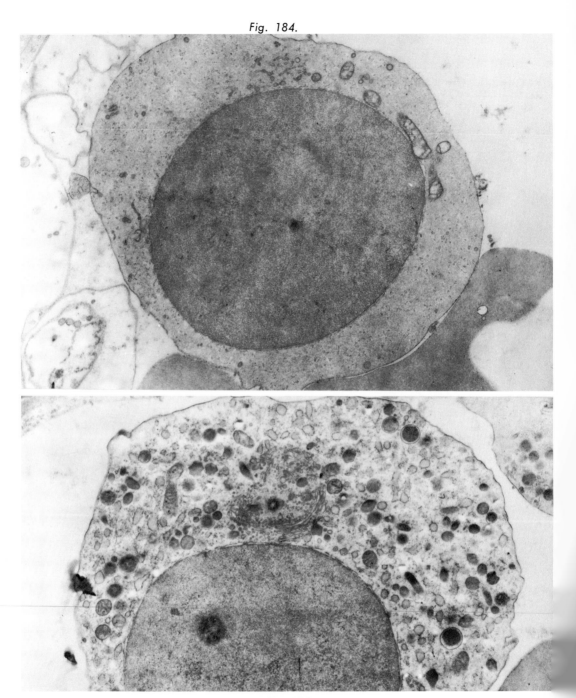

Fig. 185.

Fig. 184. Erythroblast in polychromatophylic stage. Human bone marrow, chronic lymphocytic leukemia. ✕ 14,000.

Fig. 185. Neutrophilic myelocyte. Human bone marrow, chronic lymphocytic leukemia. ✕ 16,000.

Fig. 186.

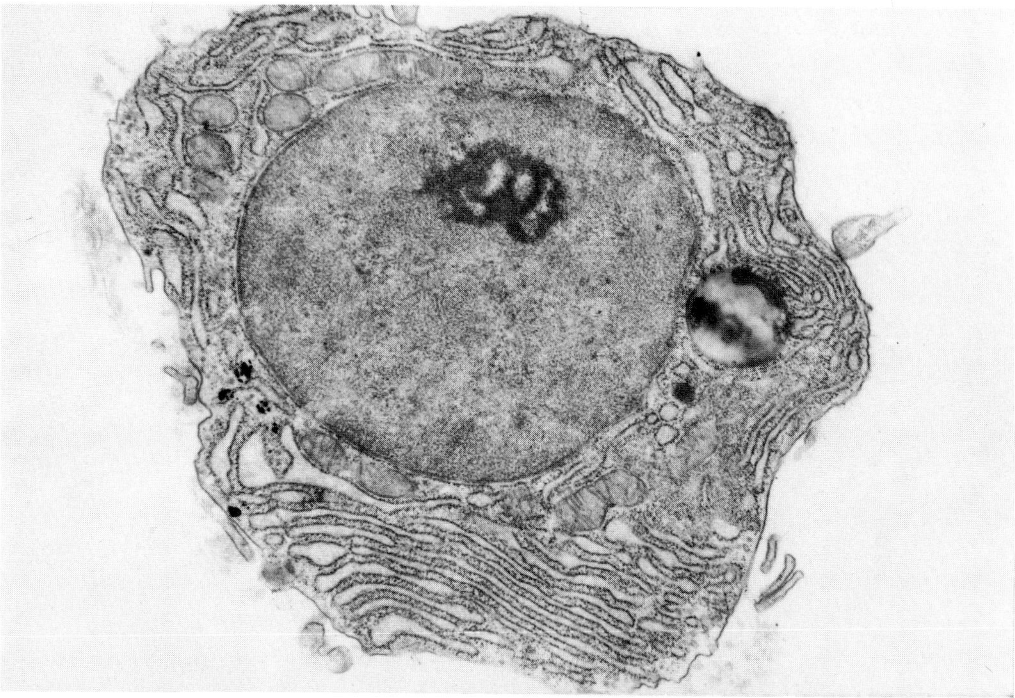

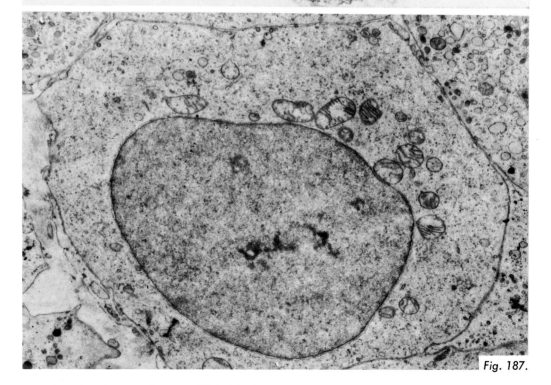

Fig. 187.

Fig. 186. Plasma cell. Dog gall bladder lamina propria. $\times$ 20,000.

Fig. 187. "Stem" cell. Human bone marrow, chronic granulocytic leukemia. $\times$ 11,000.

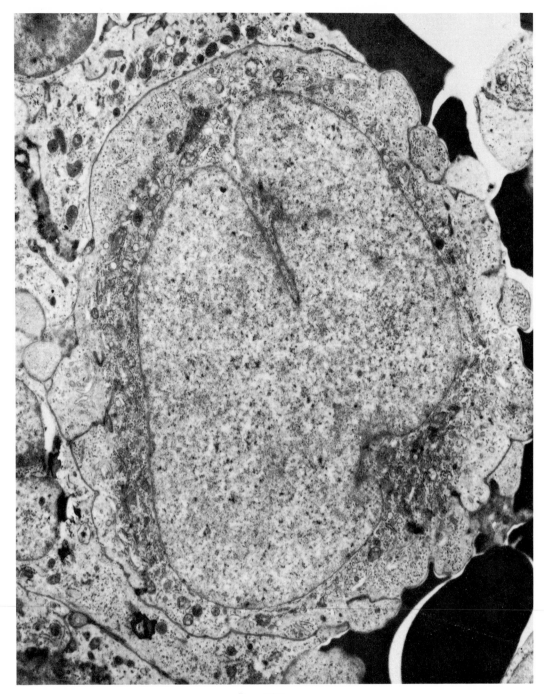

Fig. 188.

Fig. 188. Megakaryoblast developing platelet demarcation vesicles. Dog spleen. × 11,000.

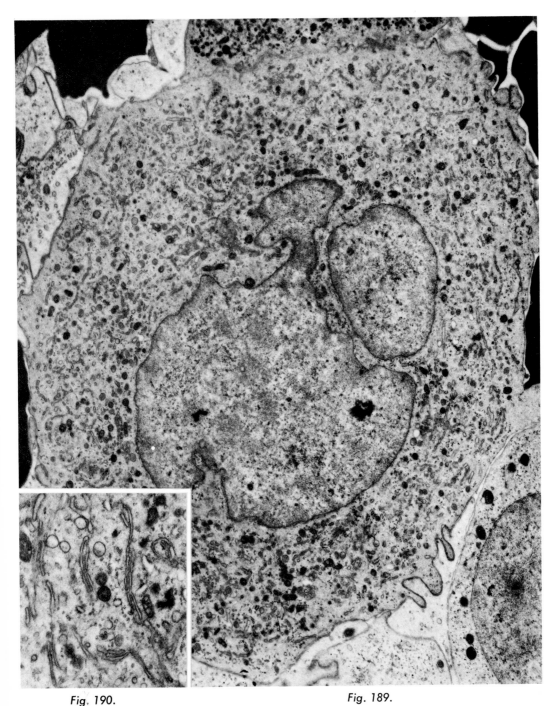

Fig. 190.   *Fig. 189.*

Fig. 189. Megakaryocyte. Dog spleen. $\times$ 12,000.

Fig. 190. Platelet demarcation membranes of megakaryocyte. Dog spleen. $\times$ 20,000.

Eosinophils

In light microscopy eosinophils are characterized by coarse, refractile, uniform sized, cytoplasmic granules that stain with acidic dyes (Fig. 180). The granules (measuring up to 1 micron) are biconvex, tripartite discs (Fig. 181). Also present in some eosinophils seen with the electron microscope are irregularly shaped, homogeneous granules comparable to the basophilic globules seen in light microscopy. The function of the latter granules is unknown. Eosinophils usually have a bilobed nucleus and contain a few more mitochondria than do neutrophils. The function of the eosinophil has not been entirely elucidated, but it is known that they are somewhat phagocytic, and they are found in large numbers in hypersensitivity (accelerated immune) reactions.

Basophils

Basophils usually have a large, bilobed nucleus (Fig. 180). Viewed with the electron microscope the cytoplasm contains coarse, dense granules that do not have a consistent pattern of internal structure (Fig. 181). The granules are known to contain histamine and heparin. Basophils display little ameboid activity. In the mudpuppy and some turtles, basophils are normally more numerous than other leukocytes. In man basophils are increased in certain pathological conditions such as chronic granulocytic leukemia, small pox, and chronic sinusitis. The function of the basophil and its relation to a similar cell (mast cell) found in loose connective tissue remains to be determined.

Lymphocytes

In light microscopy lymphocytes appear smaller than granulocytes, and they have a round nucleus and sparse basophilic cytoplasm (Fig. 180). With the electron microscope lymphocytes are seen to have sparse ergastoplasm and an indented nucleus (Fig. 182). Numerous ribosomes are scattered throughout the cytoplasm and there are relatively few large, elongate mitochondria. Most lymphocytes have a few minute granules and vacuoles (*compound vacuoles*). The function of the lymphocyte is unknown; but it is established that lymphocytes are involved in hypersensitivity and graft rejection phenomena, and that a lymphocytosis accompanies diseases which are followed by lasting immunity.

There is also a large form of lymphocyte which is about 12 microns in diameter and morphologically similar to the small lymphocyte. The motility of the larger cell is greater, and the number of granules and vacuoles is numerically greater than in the small lymphocyte. An unresolved question exists as to whether these cells are related to the monocytic series rather than the lymphocytic series.

Monocytes

Monocytes are actively motile and send out numerous pseudopods that flatten on glass, giving a larger and more irregular appearance than that of lymphocytes (Fig. 180). In light microscopy the monocyte nucleus is ovoid, kidney, or horseshoe shaped, and somewhat eccentric. The abundant cytoplasm is less basophilic than that of the small lymphocyte due to the relatively smaller number of ribosomes in the monocyte cytoplasm (Fig. 182). In electron micrographs there is an extensive tubular system of endoplasmic reticulum which gives the cell a "microvacuolated" appearance (Fig. 125). The mitochondria are small, round, and numerous. The Golgi complex is located near the nuclear indentation known as the *nuclear hof* (Fig. 62). Phagocytosed material may be seen in these cells. Occasionally homogeneous, small, membrane-lined granules (about 0.2 to 0.6 microns in diameter) can be seen in monocytes; these granules correspond to the metachromatic azurophil granules seen in the light microscope in Wright's stained blood smears. In tissue cultures the monocytes can enlarge and take on all the characteristics of macrophages (*histiocytes*); when migrating through the tissues monocytes may be indistinguishable from histiocytes (Fig. 163).

Platelets (Thrombocytes)

The platelets (*thrombocytes*) are anuclear cytoplasmic fragments which originate as detached portions of megakaryocyte cytoplasm (Fig. 180). A few small mitochondria and a sparse amount of endoplasmic reticulum are present (Fig. 182). Platelets contain a central area with specific granules (*chromomere*) and peripheral area of clear cytoplasm (*hyalomere*). The hyalomere contains serotonin and the granules contain thrombokinase (platelet factor III). The platelets function in blood coagulation.

BONE MARROW

Ontogenetically and structurally blood cells are related to and develop in a specialized form of connective tissue (bone marrow). The bone marrow is a sponge-like cavernous network of stroma and free cells, with an organization similar to that of the spleen. The majority of free cells are cells of the white blood cell (*myeloid*) and red blood cell (*erythroid*) series.

Myeloid Series

The immature cells of both the myeloid and erythroid series are indistinguishable with the electron microscope until the development of hemoglobin in the cytoplasm of the erythroid series or specific granules in the cytoplasm of the myeloid series (Figs. 184 and 185). The most immature cells (*stem cells*) have a large nucleus, many nucleoli, few ribosomes, few small mitochondria, and very few profiles of endoplasmic reticulum (Fig. 187). As the cells mature, they develop quantitatively more organelles and specific granules. Specific granules are visible in the Golgi and centrosome areas in the promyelocytic stage. By the myelocyte stage the ergastoplasm and smooth-surfaced endoplasmic reticulum are well developed, and specific granules are abundant (Fig. 185). Also by this stage one can distinguish the cells as eosinophilic, basophilic, or neutrophilic leukocytes by the fine structure

of the granules. A nucleolus may normally persist to this stage, but this occurs more often in abnormal states, such as the leukemias. As the granulocytes mature from the myelocyte stage, there is an inverse relationship between the development of specific granules on one hand, and the ergastoplasm and mitochondria on the other hand, the latter two organelles decreasing in quantity with increasing cell maturity.

Erythroid Series

The most immature erythroblasts are not easily distinguishable from their counterparts of the myeloid series until after the development of specific granules in the myeloid cells (the promyelocyte stage). Ferritin (iron particles) can be seen in the cytoplasm of erythroid cells by the polychromatophilic stage (Fig. 184). The number of ribosomes diminishes as the cells mature and there is a decrease in nuclear size with fragmentation and extrusion of the nucleus from the cell by the reticulocyte stage (Figs. 183 and 184). Persistence of portions of the nucleus and mitochondria are responsible for the reticulated appearance of near mature erythrocytes (*reticulocytes*) in the circulating blood.

Megakaryocyte Series

The megakaryocyte is a multinucleated giant cell formed by multiple nuclear divisions without corresponding cytoplasmic divisions, a condition known as polyploidy. As a result of this type of division multiple groups of centrioles can be found in this cell. In the early stages of development (megakaryoblast stage) the cytoplasm contains numerous ribosomes (Fig. 188). The ribosomes diminish in number as the cell undergoes subsequent divisions and matures (megakaryocyte stage) (Figs. 189 and 190). Megakaryocytes are identified with the electron microscope by the same features as with the light microscope: namely, large size (30 to 100 microns in diameter), extremely polymorphous nucleus, and abundant cytoplasm (Fig. 189). The cytoplasm contains numerous mitochondria that are smaller than mitochondria of monocytes. Moderately dense membrane lined granules (about 0.8 millimicrons in diameter) are scattered randomly throughout the cytoplasm. The most distinguishing feature of megakaryocytes when studied with the electron microscope is the strings of numerous, minute vesicles that coalesce to form the *platelet demarcation membranes* in the cytoplasm (Figs. 189 and 190). These membranes detach a portion of cytoplasm, with granules and mitochondria, to form the blood platelets; the platelet demarcation membranes become the plasma membranes of the platelets.

Plasma Cells (Plasmocytes)

Although plasma cells originate in lymphoid organs (lymph nodes, spleen, etc.), they are frequently found in the bone marrow. They are distinguished by abundant paralleling cisternae of ergastoplasm, which is characteristic of cells capable of protein synthesis (Fig. 186). The juxtanuclear clear zone seen with the light microscope corresponds to a highly developed Golgi complex (Figs. 180 and 186). The mitochondria of these cells are relatively large, comparable in size to those of lymphocytes. The nuclear chromatin is coarse.

The plasma cell has been identified as the cell responsible for the manufacture of gamma globulin. The synthesis of globulin takes place in the ergastoplasm; amorphous densities that occasionally can be seen within the cisternae of the ergastoplasm are thought to represent either gamma globulin or its precursor.

REFERENCES

Blood

BIMES, C.: Le Lymphocyte. Problèmes d'actualité. Bull. Assoc. Anat., 48:1–132, 1962.

BRAUNSTEINER, H., and D. ZUCKER-FRANKLIN: *The Physiology and Pathology of Leukocytes.* Grune & Stratton, New York, 1962.

GOODMAN, J., E. REILLY, and R. MOORE: Electron microscopy of formed elements of normal human blood. Blood 12:428–442, 1957.

LOW, F., and J. FREEMAN: *Electron Microscopic Atlas of Normal and Leukemic Human Blood.* McGraw-Hill Book Company, New York, 1958.

REBUCK, J., A. PETZ, J. RIDDLE, R. PRIEST, and G. LO GRIPPO: Human leukocyte functions in the tissues, in *Biological Activity of the Leucocyte,* Ciba Foundation Study Group No. 10, edited by G. Wolstenholme and M. O'Connor, pp. 3–26. Little, Brown and Company, Boston, 1961.

SCHULZ, H.: Serotoninbestimmungen an thrombocyten und an fraktionen von thrombocyten. Klin. Woch., 41:343–344, 1963.

SENO, S., K. YOSHIZAWA, T. NAKAMOTO and S. KANDA: A morphologic study of reticulocytes with special reference to the substantia granulofilamentosa. Folia Hemat., 2:269–279, 1958.

WATANABE, Y.: Observations of white blood cells with electron microscope. J. Electronmic., 5:46–57, 1957.

WEDELL, J., and H. SCHULZ: Über fettphagocytose der thrombocytes des menschen. Klin. Woch., 41:343, 1963.

Bone Marrow

ACKERMAN, G., A. GRASSO, and R. KNOUFF: Erythropoiesis in the mammalian embryonic liver as revealed by electron microscopy. Lab. Invest., 10:787–796, 1961.

BESSIS, M.: Ultrastructure of lymphoid and plasma cells in relation to globulin and antibody formation. Lab. Invest., 10:1040–1067, 1961.

BESSIS, M., and J. THIÉRY: Electron microscopy of human white blood cells and their stem cells. Intern. Rev. Cytol., 12:199–242, 1961.

PEASE, D.: An electron microscope study of red bone marrow. J. Hemat., 11:501–526, 1956.

SENO, S.: The structure and the function of reticulocyte. Acta Haemat. Japon., Suppl. 2, 21:171–181, 1958.

YAMADA, E.: The fine structure of the megakaryocyte in the mouse spleen. Acta Anat., 29:267–290, 1957.

INDEX